Register Now for Or
to Your Bo

Your print purchase of *Strategic Planning in Healthcare* **includes online access to the contents of your book**—increasing accessibility, portability, and searchability!

Access today at:

http://connect.springerpub.com/content/book/978-0-8261-6484-1
or scan the QR code at the right with your smartphone
and enter the access code below.

WJ5M542M

Scan here for quick access.

If you are experiencing problems accessing the digital component of this product, please contact our customer service department at cs@springerpub.com

The online access with your print purchase is available at the publisher's discretion and may be removed at any time without notice.

Publisher's Note: New and used products purchased from third-party sellers are not guaranteed for quality, authenticity, or access to any included digital components.

STRATEGIC PLANNING IN HEALTHCARE

Brian C. Martin, PhD, MBA, is Professor, Associate Dean for Administration, and Director of Graduate Programs in Public Health in the School of Health Professions at Eastern Virginia Medical School (EVMS). He has operational and administrative responsibilities for the MPH degree. As an academician, Dr. Martin has taught undergraduate and graduate students, provided service activities, and conducted research in the area of health services administration for over 15 years. His research interests include access to care, financing healthcare services, cost/benefit analysis, and healthcare workforce development. Prior to entering academia, he performed strategic planning and new business development in a large nonprofit, tertiary care, teaching hospital. Dr. Martin earned his BBA (1988) and MBA (1993) degrees from the University of South Carolina School of Business. He earned his PhD in Health Services Research and Administration (1996) from the University of South Carolina School of Public Health.

STRATEGIC PLANNING IN HEALTHCARE

AN INTRODUCTION FOR HEALTH PROFESSIONALS

Brian C. Martin, PhD, MBA

Springer Publishing Company, LLC
11 West 42nd Street
New York, NY 10036
www.springerpub.com

Acquisitions Editor: David D'Addona
Compositor: Exeter Premedia Services Private Ltd.

ISBN: 9780826164834
ebook ISBN: 9780826164841

Instructors' Materials: Qualified instructors may request supplements by emailing textbook@springerpub.com:
Instructors' Manual ISBN: 9780826164711
Instructors' PowerPoints ISBN: 9780826164735
Instructors' Test Bank ISBN: 9780826164728

Student Resources are available for download from http://www.springerpub.com/sph
Student Resources: Sample Strategic Plans ISBN: 9780826164742
Student Resources: Worksheets ISBN: 9780826164759

18 19 20 21 22 / 5 4 3 2 1

Library of Congress Cataloging-in-Publication Data

Names: Martin, Brian C., author.
Title: Strategic planning in healthcare: an introduction for health professionals / Brian C. Martin.
Description: New York, NY: Springer Publishing Company, LLC, [2019] | Includes bibliographical references and index.
Identifiers: LCCN 2018026440 | ISBN 9780826164834 | ISBN 9780826164841 (ebook) | ISBN 9780826164711 (instructors' manual) | ISBN 9780826164735 (instructors' PowerPoints) | ISBN 9780826164728 (instructors' test bank) | ISBN 9780826164742 (student resources: sample strategic plans) | ISBN 9780826164759 (student resources: worksheets)
Subjects: | MESH: Strategic Planning | Health Planning | Health Services | United States
Classification: LCC RA394.9 | NLM W 84 AA1 | DDC 362.1—dc23
LC record available at https://lccn.loc.gov/2018026440

Printed in the United States of America.

CONTENTS

PREFACE

I have taught strategic planning over the past 20 years to public health students, drawing heavily on my previous planning experience in a large non-profit hospital. My biggest challenge has been finding a text that explains the planning process in a concise manner that is easily understood by students who are naïve to the planning process, and yet can allow students to cultivate the skills necessary to develop a strategic plan. This book is a culmination of years of teaching and professional experience, feedback from students, and input from professionals in the field.

My constant focus for this text has been to develop a tool that can be used to teach strategic planning through both a theoretical and an application perspective. I want readers to be able to learn concepts and then to be able to apply those concepts in a practical way. Complex healthcare organizations require leaders who understand the need and value of strategic planning, and it is my hope that future leaders who use this text are better prepared to face challenges.

LEARNING TOOLS

This book incorporates a number of features that are designed to optimize learning. A strong theoretical framework provides the background from which learners can draw in understanding a common case that threads through each chapter. The chapters are organized to follow the strategic planning cycle, from reviewing the Mission Statement to Evaluation and Control. The importance of each step in the cycle is explained, and concrete tools are provided to complete each activity. Peppered throughout the text are practical examples of how concepts are applied and the impact of decision making.

Readers can then apply what they have learned using chapter-specific worksheets to develop individual components of a strategic plan. In completing the worksheets for each chapter, a reader will be writing his or her own quasi-strategic plan. This hands-on learning opportunity allows students to maximize their knowledge, moving up the pyramid in Bloom's taxonomy and transforming understanding into creation.

INSTRUCTORS' RESOURCES

Course instructors will have several resources available to them as they lead students to develop strategic planning skills. **Qualified instructors may request instructors' materials by email: textbook@springerpub.com. Student resources are available for download from http://www.springerpub.com/sph.**

- PowerPoint files for each chapter reinforce salient points and allow for discussion.
- Worksheets for each of the steps in the strategic planning process guide students in writing a quasi-strategic plan.
- Sample strategic plans provide examples beyond the textbook and prompt discussions in the classroom and student groups.
- A test bank of questions, including multiple-choice, true/false, and short-answer essay questions, assesses learning and progression.

INTENDED AUDIENCES

This book is intended to be used as a required text for an undergraduate or graduate course that introduces students to the strategic planning process. As such, it is a "soups to nuts" strategic planning text, and instructors will not need supplemental texts in order to engage their students. The end goal is to use didactic and practical experiential learning to train future organizational leaders who are thoroughly competent planners.

Public health students with a track or concentration in health management and policy or community health (or similarly named "tracks/concentrations") will benefit from this learning. Additionally, the text can be a crucial component of training for healthcare administration (business administration) students, as well as students in nursing and allied health programs. A course using this text could be offered during any semester but would typically follow an introductory health administration course.

CONTENTS

Each chapter begins with a quote from a thought leader that relates the importance of planning, followed by five learning objectives. Next is a nonhealthcare vignette that describes a situation where the concepts of the chapter will be applied. After the material is presented, a common case study (throughout this text, it will be the fictitious "Memorial Hospital, Inc.") is used to apply each chapter's material in a real-world healthcare setting. Chapters 2 to 7 contain planning process worksheets, which readers can complete based on a real-life or fictitious organization. A glossary and reference list round out the materials for each chapter.

Chapter 1 describes the function of planning and why it is important to decision making in healthcare organizations. The origins of planning, application to healthcare, and types of plans are explained, and practical advantages and disadvantages of planning are reviewed. Chapter 2 provides an overview of the strategic planning process, including fundamental steps in the process, the influence of leadership, and the impact of quality improvement.

Chapters 3 to 7 describe each of the steps in the strategic planning process in detail. Chapter 3 discusses organizational purpose and the importance of an organization's mission to its planning and operational activities. The relationship of mission, vision, and values is explained, and the impact of these statements is discussed. Chapter 4 introduces the importance of a situational analysis to inform future direction and plans. A strengths, weaknesses, opportunities, and threats (SWOT) analysis is used for this purpose, and tools are introduced to manage an organization from its current state to its desired state.

Chapter 5 describes the importance of setting objectives, both short and long term, and why there might be resistance to setting organizational objectives. A structure is used to walk readers through the process of developing and writing objectives that maximize efficiency and effectiveness. Accomplishing objectives through the development and implementation of strategies and operational plans is the topic of Chapter 6. The relationship of strategies to objectives, methods for evaluating an organization's products and services, and the role of budgeting are included. Chapter 7 describes the feedback loop in the strategic planning process—evaluation and control. The importance of viewing strategic planning as a continuous process, and common tools that are used to evaluate and improve plans, are incorporated. Finally, a sampling of strategic plans is included for reference in Chapter 8.

In the end, a reader of this book will have the knowledge and skills needed to lead a strategic planning process in an organization. It is my hope that those who use this textbook will continue to learn and develop the art of strategic planning as they make contributions to the future of their organizations and their professions.

ACKNOWLEDGMENTS

No person achieves a position of professional or academic standing without the support of many colleagues, family, and friends. My own development includes too many individuals to list separately. I stand on their shoulders. I would also be remiss in failing to acknowledge the many students with whom I have had the pleasure to interact in my career, both at East Tennessee State University and at Eastern Virginia Medical School, and who have taught me at least as much as I have taught them.

For the writing of this textbook, I would like to specifically acknowledge Drs. Mark Bittle, Mike Stoots, Reinetta Waldrop, and Nizar Wehbi for their edits and suggestions for the development of the chapters, and Ryan Ross for his consultation and expertise.

Finally, I would like to recognize the important contributions of the publisher's staff, particularly David D'Addona and Jaclyn Shultz. Their expertise and guidance were invaluable in turning a teacher into an author.

CHAPTER 1

PLANNING: WHAT IS IT AND WHY IS IT IMPORTANT?

By failing to prepare, you are preparing to fail.

—Benjamin Franklin
Founding father, inventor, father of time management

LEARNING OBJECTIVES

1. Understand the importance of planning in healthcare organizations.
2. Describe the five management functions and their importance in decision making.
3. Understand the origins of planning and its application to organizations.
4. Differentiate between strategic, tactical, operational, and contingency plans.
5. Explain the advantages and disadvantages of planning in the healthcare industry.

Sophia is an undergraduate student studying public health at State University. She is also the president of the State University self-contained underwater breathing apparatus (SCUBA) Club, which sponsors an annual dive trip to the Florida Keys during fall break. The trip is a highlight of the year for the club, and for students who look forward to diving pristine freshwater springs on the way to the Keys and the warm ocean waters surrounding the archipelago. Sophia has been a certified diver since her junior open water course at age 12, and is confident of her ability to plan the dive excursions in Florida. However, she is new to a leadership position and just became president of the SCUBA Club in the last spring semester. As she sits at her laptop working to develop a promotional flyer for the trip, Sophia realizes that there are many logistical questions that need to be answered before she can market the trip.

"Plan your dive, dive your plan." Sophia recalls her dive instructor, Mike, repeating this phrase often during her certification courses. Recreational SCUBA diving is very safe, but only if a diver develops detailed plans following strict guidelines for each dive. Can she apply the same concepts to plan a successful dive trip for the club? Sophia knows that the members would like a safe, fun, affordable dive trip. She opens a new Word document and types the heading "Planning the annual dive trip," and begins a list of bullet points.

- Travel
  - Airplane
    - *Pros:* Fast (maximize dive days), convenient
    - *Cons*: Expensive, shouldn't dive within 24 hours of flying, can't transport air tanks
  - Drive university van
    - *Pros:* Up to 15 passengers, university covers breakdowns and maintenance, can transport dive gear, can dive on arrival and right up to departure, fun time
    - *Cons*: Driver must be a university employee, charge to rent the van and surcharge for gas, slow (will take 2 days each way)
  - Drive personal cars
    - *Pros:* Four to six students per car, cheapest alternative, can dive on arrival and right up to departure, fun time
    - *Cons*: Owner of car responsible for breakdowns and maintenance, slow (will take 2 days each way)

Sophia scratches her head—this may be more challenging than she thought! She decides to enlist the officers for a brainstorming session. Balancing safety, fun, and affordability is important to the club members and essential to planning a successful trip.

While Sophia is engaged in event planning, she is learning what leaders in all organizations, small and large, must recognize—planning is an essential element for success. You do not want to answer the question "Where are we going?" with "I don't know, but we're making great time!"

■ ■ ■

PLANNING: A MANAGEMENT FUNCTION

Koontz and O'Donnell described management as having five functions: planning, organizing, staffing, directing/leading, and controlling (Koontz & O'Donnell, 1976). While it may be convenient to discuss these functions separately, it is important to note that they are highly inseparable and overlapping in practice. Each function is a dedicated component in the field of management, and an effective manager is well versed in each of these areas.

Planning is the managerial function concerned with creating a detailed blueprint that, when implemented, is meant to achieve specific organizational objectives. The details of the plan identify what will be performed, when, and by whom. It includes identifying a desired future and the means to achieve that future. Since the future is unknown and the internal and external environments within which the organization operates are constantly changing, planning must be a continuous process. Henri Fayol, one of the earliest management theorists, considered planning to be the most difficult function that managers complete.

Organizing the resources required to complete the objectives identified in the plan is the next managerial function. As such, organizing requires recognition that organizational objectives often compete for scarce resources, identification of the organization's limited resources, and assignment of those resources to planned activities. Similar to a conductor coordinating an orchestra, a manager coordinates the resources at his or her disposal to best meet the needs of the organization. In the end, organizing helps ensure efficiency and effectiveness.

While organizing includes allocating resources to tasks, **staffing** specifically addresses the human resource component and the relationship to planned objectives. Healthcare is a service industry and, therefore, personnel-intensive. Having the right people in the right place at the right time is essential to meeting organizational objectives, and to guarantee that the organization can function effectively.

Directing is a key managerial role that deals with human resources from a motivational and communication perspective. While organizing and staffing get the pieces in place, directing is the process of inspiring employees to complete tasks for the organization in such a way that the human resource is maximized—in a word, directing and leading requires leadership.

Controlling is the feedback loop that managers use to ensure that organizational objectives are being addressed and met as planned. Setting objectives and tasking resources to complete those objectives serves only to get the ball rolling. Along the way, managers need to examine the process that is being followed to complete the objectives, surveying milestones along the way, and guaranteeing that appropriate steps are being taken to move the process toward completion.

These five functions of management work together to identify organizational objectives and drive resources toward the satisfaction of those objectives. Each function affects the performance of the others, as depicted in Figure 1.1, and is used by managers at all levels within an organization to make decisions.

As we look at strategic planning and how it is applied in the health professions, you will learn how planning often serves as the tie that binds these functions together. As such, it is essential to organizational success.

WHY IS PLANNING IMPORTANT?

As Sophia struggled with planning her club dive trip, one thing she kept in mind was the desires of the club members—a safe, fun, affordable dive trip. Planning drives managers to ask the fundamental question "What do we want

FIGURE 1.1 Management Functions and Decision Making

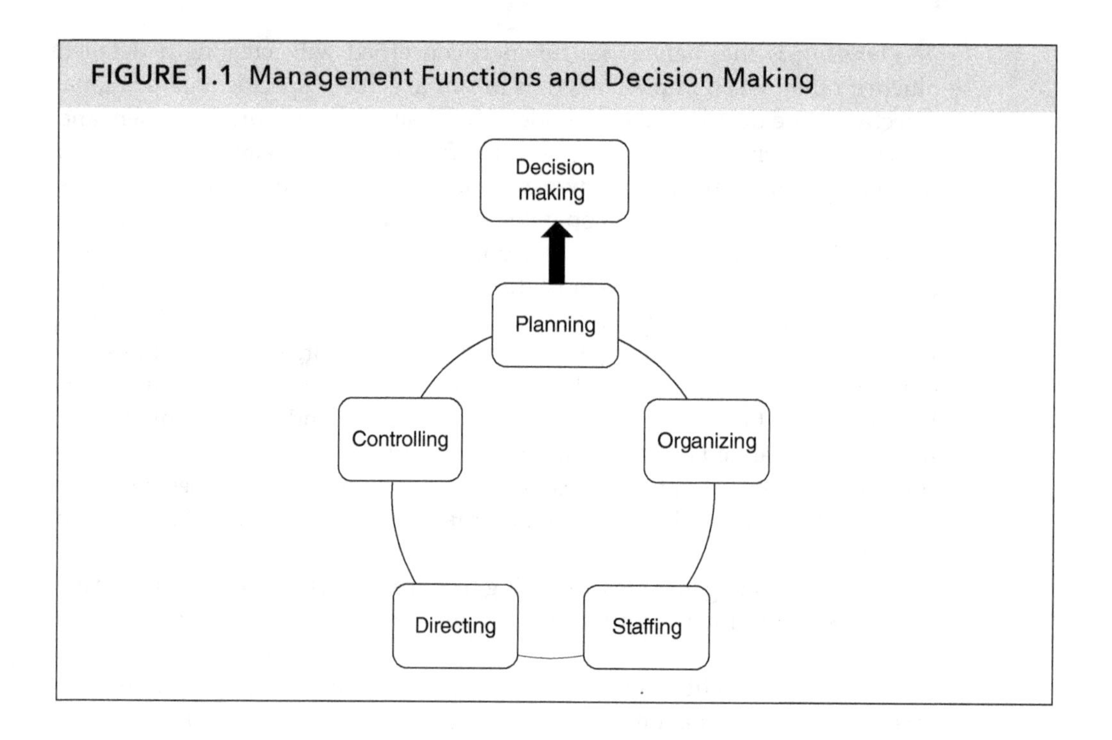

to achieve?" and then leads them to create road maps to accomplish what is desired. A significant outcome of the process is a laser focus on what will drive the organization to succeed. Questions such as Why did we invest in this service line, yet it isn't being used?, Why do our revenues continue to miss our projections?, and Why has the **board** asked me to resign? may be indicators that an organization lacks strategic planning.

A healthcare organization without a **long-term planning** perspective runs the risk of deviating from its goals and its ability to satisfy its corporate purpose. Long-term success is crucial for any organization to survive, and a critical factor for success is how well the organization can plan for future events and activities. Given that all organizations operate with finite resources (e.g., capital, cash, personnel), allocation of those resources must be done purposefully in order to maximize efficiency and effectiveness. Managers face multiple options for competing projects, which will each add some benefit to the organization. Understanding the organization and the environment in which it operates allows managers to assign resources appropriately.

Planning is, by definition, proactive (you cannot plan for something that has already occurred). It allows you to see where you want to go and to identify potential hazards along the way, an important part of risk management. It also allows for course correction when things are not going according to plan, an important part of organizational effectiveness. Planning is not perfect—no one has the ability to predict the future. However, the process of planning is rooted in a systematic evaluation of potential futures that identifies market forces that will affect the course of the organization. The outcome of planning is a strategic direction that will counter those market forces that would hamper the organization and take advantage of those that will further its goals.

The importance of planning has been championed by notable people across history.

> You've got to come up with a plan. You can't wish things will get better.
>
> —*John "Jack" F. Welch*
> *CEO of General Electric (1981–2001)*

> A plan is not putting you in a box and forcing you to stay there. A plan is a guide to keep you on course, efficient, and safe.
>
> —*Amber Hurdle*
> *Business coach/Speaker*

> The company without a strategy is willing to try anything.
>
> —*Michael Porter*
> *Academic, business strategy theorist*

> Failure is the most effective technique to optimize strategic planning, implementation, and processes.
>
> —*Thomas A. Edison*
> *Inventor, businessman*

> The sole purpose of strategic planning is to enable the company to gain, as effectively as possible, a sustainable advantage over its competitors.
>
> —*Kenichi Ohmae*
> *Organizational theorist, management consultant*

While planning has been recognized as a foundational management function for hundreds of years, long-term planning was adopted by U.S. businesses *en masse* during the 1950s in response to a need to project revenues based on future sales. Long-term planning has the underlying assumption that a business will continue to produce the same goods/services that it has produced in the past. However, volatility within the industry and/or market meant that a business would need the flexibility to adapt its goods/services to changing demands. Recognizing that forces within the organization and in the environment, both those that can be controlled and those that cannot, influence future success, business leaders accepted that specific tactics would need to be developed to account for this volatility. And for that they looked to lessons etched in history.

Military Foundations of Planning

The concept of strategy had its beginnings in military applications hundreds of years ago. Sun Tzu (544–496 BCE) was a Chinese general and military strategist during the Age of Warring States, a period when seven states fought for survival and control of China. Sun Tzu's tremendous success on the battlefield was due, in large part, to his knowledge of strategy and leadership, and how those principles could be applied in preparing for a successful military campaign. He shared the wisdom he gained over years of battles in his book *The Art of War* (Sun Tzu & Griffith, 1964), which has been recognized by military leaders throughout history as essential reading. The importance of strategy in a military application was summed up by Sun Tzu when he said: "Victorious warriors win first and then go to war, while defeated warriors go to war first and then seek to win."

Homer, Euripides, and other early strategists and writers also discussed the principles and applications of strategy. The foundation of our word "strategy" comes from the Greek word *stratēgōs*, which means "a general." And the Greek verb *stratēgēō* means "to plan the destruction of one's enemies through effective use of resources" (Bracker, 1980).

Replace the term "enemies" with "competition" and you have the business application of strategy that became widespread beginning in the 1960s. The focus of strategic planning during that time was on financial planning and responding to the environment and organizations in a specific market. However, during the 1980s, business leaders expanded strategic planning to include the philosophy of strategic management, in recognition that strategy must be continuously evaluated and managed in order to be successful. We will see this philosophy as we explore the process of strategic planning and the implementation of strategic plans as "living" documents.

ADAPTING TO CHANGING CIRCUMSTANCES: THE CASE OF AMERICAN EXPRESS COMPANY

You may know American Express Company (aka, American Express or Amex) as the multinational financial services company that it is today, or you may know it as a consumer credit card lending company. But did you know that it had very different beginnings? The original company was founded as an association of investors in 1850 when three existing companies were consolidated. The three companies provided express transport services moving mail, goods, and valuables across markets in the United States, and the consolidation allowed for expansion and tremendous financial success. In 1866, Merchants Union Express Company entered the market as a competitor, and the rival companies were driven to near bankruptcy due to ruthless competition. In 1868, the two competitors merged to form the American Merchants Union Express Company, which was renamed American Express Company in 1873.

In 1881, after a leadership change, new product innovations were introduced, including the American Express Money Order (1882), the American Express Travelers Cheque (1891), the first European office in Paris (1895), international services (late 1800s/early 1900s), and travel services (1915). In response to the U.S. federal government nationalization of the express industry in 1918, American Express Company consolidated its service offerings to its banking and travel operations. The highly recognizable American Express green charge card was introduced in 1958. From the 1960s through the 1980s, American Express Company acquired (and often sold) investment banking, insurance, and publishing companies. By the early 21st century, American Express Company operated in more than 40 countries. In 2016,

(*continued*)

(continued)

Interbrand ranked American Express as the 25th most valuable brand in the world, with an estimated net worth of $18.358 billion.

American Express evolved in response to changes in the market, including the impact of governmental regulation. An important part of the planning process is assessing the environment in which an organization does business.

Many corporations completing environmental assessments find that changes in the healthcare market bring opportunities for expansion into that market. For example, Walmart Inc., a multinational retail corporation that includes in-store pharmacies and vision centers, has been implementing a strategy to develop in-store health clinics and to acquire a healthcare insurance product. CVS Health, a retail pharmacy chain, is also planning to acquire a health insurance company.

1. Why would a business such as Walmart, Inc. be interested in entering the healthcare provider market?
2. Why would a business such as CVS Health be interested in moving beyond its market as a retail pharmacy to enter the health insurance market?

TYPES OF PLANS

The model for strategic planning in healthcare and other sectors has remained relatively unchanged over time. In the late 1980s, Simyar, Lloyd-Jones, and Caro (1988) composed an ordered sequence for healthcare strategic planning:

- Identify the organization's current position, including present mission, long-term objectives, strategies, and policies.
- Analyze the environment.
- Conduct an organizational audit.
- Identify the various alternative strategies based on relevant data.
- Select the best alternative.
- Gain acceptance.
- Prepare long- and short-range plans to support and carry out the strategy.
- Implement the plan and conduct ongoing evaluation.

There are many types of plans; however, most plans can be broadly categorized as "strategic," "tactical," or "operational." The differences in these types of plans are centered on length of time and responsibility level within the organization (see Figure 1.2). **Strategic plans** are written to cover a longer period of time. While most healthcare strategic plans in the 1980s were written for 10-year periods, that time has been significantly shortened to 5 years or less today. Strategic plans fall within the realm of executive management, due to their broad scope and influence on the very nature of the organization. **Tactical plans** cover a mid-length period of time, typically 1 to 2 years, and are implemented by mid-level management. **Operational plans** are written to

FIGURE 1.2 Type of Plans Relative to Time and Organizational Responsibility

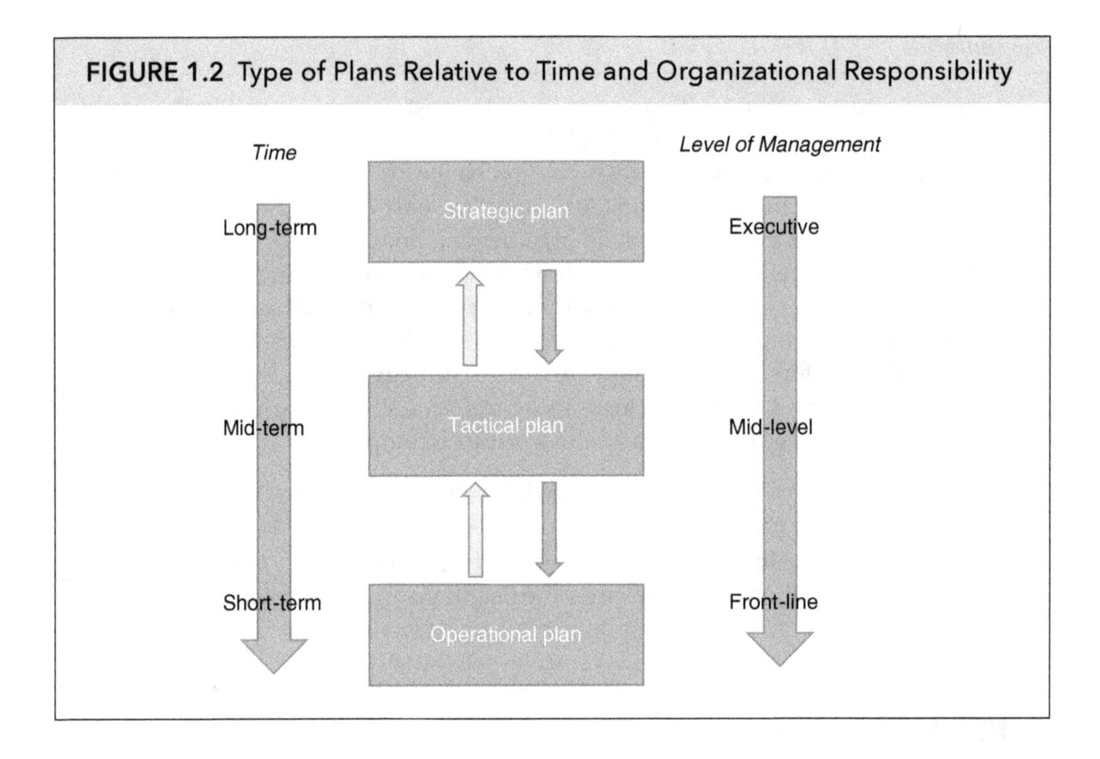

cover activities within a 12-month period, and are executed by frontline management. Ideally, each plan fits into and is guided by the one above it.

Many healthcare organizations operate a more abbreviated planning cycle and use only strategic and operational plans. Strategic planning in larger organizations may also be organized around three levels: corporate strategy, product or service line strategy, and functional area strategy. Organizing around corporate strategy recognizes that an organization has multiple businesses or divisions that operate under a parent organization. In order to maximize value for the parent organizations, each business or division should conduct strategic plans that contribute to and work in concert with the parent organization. Organizing according to product or service line focuses on the significance of the different product/service lines to the organization and seeks to maximize effectiveness of those areas. Similarly, organizing strategic planning around functional areas recognizes the importance of conducting planning activities that maximize the value of those areas. In all cases, approval and resourcing of an organization's plans require executive management and board consent. In general, a board for a not-for-profit organization is referred to as a **Board of Trustees** and a board for a for-profit organization is referred to as a **Board of Directors**.

Once a plan is created, there must be a purposeful effort to implement the plan. Since planning is a widespread organizational activity, involving employees at every level of the organization, there is generally a tremendous amount of momentum at the end of the process. This point is critical for executive management in that it must remember that the purpose of strategic planning is not to create a product (the plan) but to develop a process by which the organization will operate. Many organizations have failed to take this next all-important step, leaving plans sitting unused on shelves until the next planning cycle. In order to avoid having a worthless plan, executive management must implement and actively manage the plan, instilling this process as a part of the corporate culture of the organization.

Managing the implementation of the strategic plan requires that management view the process and the unfolding future without blinders. It is tempting to recall the tremendous amount of effort and resources that went into developing a plan, and then to simply "pull the trigger" and watch as the plan unfolds. However, leaders must remember that plans were developed with conditions of uncertainty in a volatile environment, and that those plans will be implemented in a continuously evolving setting. Therefore, an important part of managing the implementation of the strategic plan is continuously monitoring the internal and external environments and adapting the plan to the situation.

PLANNING FOR THE PLANNING

A review of the planning process and types of plans reveals that there are a lot of moving parts that must be synchronized in order for planning to be successful. Preparing for the strategic planning process increases the impact that the plan will have on the organization. It must be clear that the process is supported from the very top of the organization, and the board and chief executive officer (**CEO**) should communicate the importance and significance of the planning process to the entire organization. The planning team should be announced, as well as the expectation that all departments/units will participate in the process. Many organizations use a facilitator for the process—either someone within the organization who has training and experience, or a consultant. If a facilitator is used, that person should also be introduced by the CEO.

Early in the process, a schedule of activities should be developed and specific milestones identified. Sources of historic data and relevant databases should be secured, and the status of the most recent strategic plan should be thoroughly reviewed. Important external stakeholders should also be identified as early as possible, and the planning procedure communicated to them, to ensure that their important perspectives are captured during the process. Finally, strategic planning orientation meetings can be very helpful in reinforcing the previous communications and in bringing together the people who will be integral to success.

PLANNING COMPLICATIONS IN THE HEALTHCARE INDUSTRY

The focus of this book is strategic planning and management in the healthcare industry, which is made up of many sectors dedicated to providing goods and services to patients through preventive, curative, rehabilitative, and palliative care. U.S. healthcare spending increased 4.3% to $3.3 trillion in 2016, amounting to $10,348 per capita (Centers for Medicare & Medicaid Services, 2018). Total healthcare expenditures in the United States have grown tremendously over the past 50 years (see Figure 1.3).

The share of gross domestic product (GDP) related to healthcare spending has also increased dramatically, reaching 17.9% in 2016 projected to reach 20%

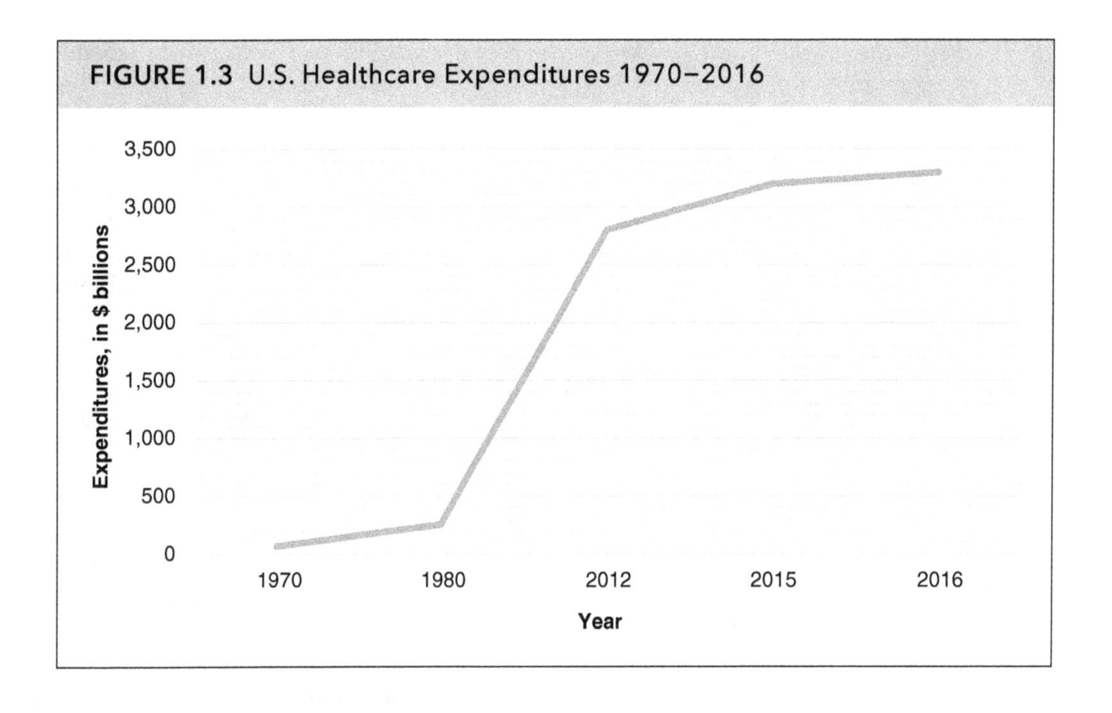

FIGURE 1.3 U.S. Healthcare Expenditures 1970–2016

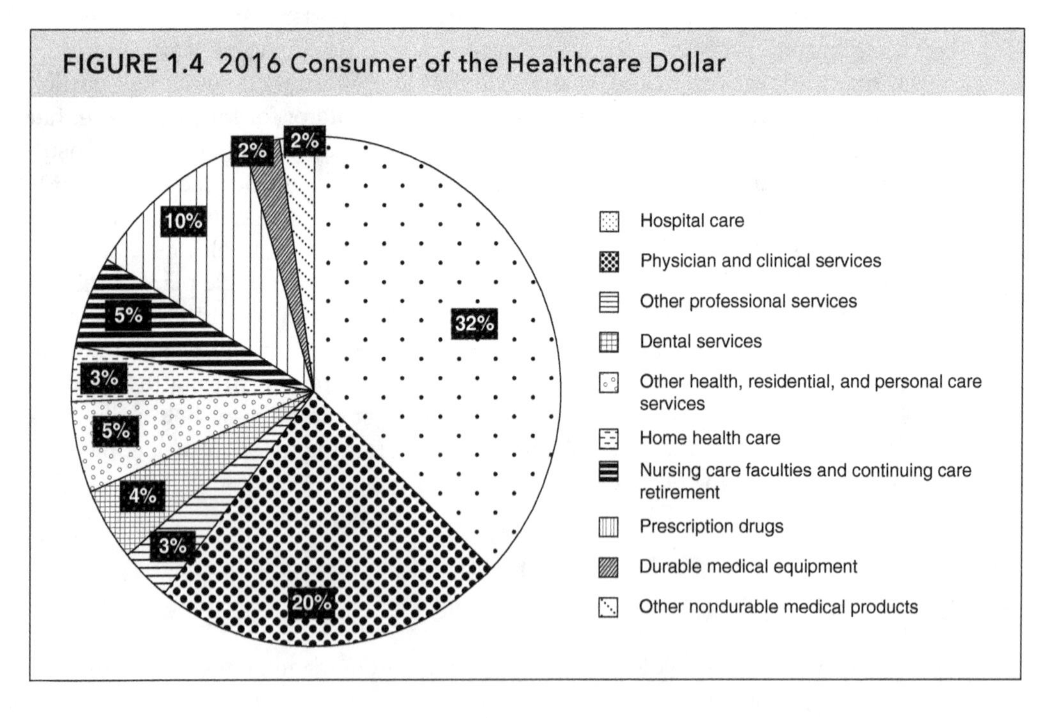

FIGURE 1.4 2016 Consumer of the Healthcare Dollar

in 2025. That means that $1 of every $5 of goods and services produced in the United States will be related to healthcare in the year 2025. The majority of the healthcare dollars were spent on hospital and physician/clinical services in 2016 (see Figure 1.4).

For our purposes, the term "healthcare" is defined broadly and includes, but is not limited to, the following:

- Teaching hospitals
- Community hospitals
- Specialty hospitals
- Multispecialty group practices
- Solo practices
- Large group practices
- Small group practices
- Long-term care facilities
- Home health agencies
- Integrated delivery systems
- Health insurance companies
- Managed care organizations
- Durable medical equipment manufacturers
- Pharmaceutical companies
- Pharmacies
- State and local departments of public health
- Ancillary support services, such as laboratory, radiology, physical therapy, and so on

Strategic management in healthcare organizations developed 35 to 40 years ago. The lag in application of strategic management in the healthcare sector was driven largely by the fact that services were historically reimbursed on a fee-for-service, cost-plus basis, which insulated healthcare organizations and executives against decisions that would be considered detrimental under different reimbursement scenarios. Through the 1970s, most planning activities were centered on capital expansion (e.g., creation of new buildings and equipment) and funding service expansion to meet the needs of growing populations. This situation was altered significantly with the passage of the Social Security Amendments Act of 1983, which created Medicare's Inpatient Prospective Payment System (IPPS) for inpatient hospital payments. The emphasis during this time period was to build services to generate revenues. The heavy influence of managed care in private markets in the 1980s and 1990s added additional strain, during a period of concurrent cost increases and intensified competition, that caused healthcare organizations to focus on strategies that maximized reimbursement. Additional payment modifications soon followed, in both the public (governmental) and private insurance markets. Substantial decreases in reimbursements demanded that healthcare executives apply strategic management principles.

Today, healthcare professionals operate in an ever-changing environment that threatens organizational survival. Carrying out the purpose of the organization, meeting demands of stakeholders, maintaining and growing market share in a competitive environment, adapting to laws and regulations, adjusting services to changing population demographics, operating in an environment of scarce resources, leveraging differentiated services, and managing the departure of key employees/physicians are all challenges that can overwhelm an organization and endanger success. Strategies that focus on likely contingencies are required in this dynamic environment.

The planning activity itself demands significant amounts of time and other resources, assets that can be considered spent frivolously when an organization is focused on operational activities and crisis management. There is an obvious delay in planning activities now and the operational benefits in the future, and those benefits are not always apparent and/or appreciated. Therefore, having a management team and governing body that appreciates the value of planning is a foundational requirement for the planning process.

Healthcare is made up of multiple provider organizations with tremendous variation in size and complexity. Examples of large providers include state/local health departments, multihospital systems, academic medical centers, multispecialty physician practices, integrated delivery systems, Accountable Care Organizations (ACOs), pharmacy chains, multiproduct health insurance companies, managed care organizations, and pharmacy benefit management companies. Examples of small providers include single and small group physician practices, independent pharmacies, home healthcare providers, and durable medical equipment companies. Some healthcare organizations, particularly those that are smaller, lack leadership and staff that are trained and/or experienced in strategic planning. In those cases, developing an effective strategic plan is not something that the organization can complete alone. Fortunately, there is an abundance of strategic planning resources available through professional associations and other sources, as well as consultants who work with organizations of all types and sizes.

Larger organizations often complete the planning process through teams. These teams assist the CEO by scanning and monitoring the internal and external environments, developing goals and strategies for the organization, coordinating the process among the different units within the organization, and providing leadership and training to other managers within the organization. The advantages of planning teams include distribution of the workload ("many hands make light work"), synergy associated with the wisdom of the group versus the individual, and the ability to objectively analyze situations while minimizing political and turf issues.

PLANNING: ADVANTAGES AND DISADVANTAGES FOR HEALTHCARE ORGANIZATIONS

One of the primary advantages of strategic planning is to make sure that everyone knows why the organization exists and what it is trying to accomplish. Strategic plans are great communication tools, and the process itself can be used to cement common purpose and shared values. Specific organizational goals and objectives can be developed and shared both horizontally and vertically within the organization, setting clear expectations for the management team and unifying staff in a singular purpose.

As we will discuss, the strategic planning process provides a road map to guide the organization in the dynamic healthcare environment. It allows for honest assessment of the organization (**internal assessment**) and the environment in which it operates (**external assessment**), allowing for potential threats to be anticipated and opportunities to be identified in the market. While all threats cannot be predicted, investments in planning activities increase the likelihood that management can focus more of its time on daily operations and less of its time on crisis containment. Decision making becomes more consistent and more likely to enhance future performance.

There is always more that an organization could do if it had more funding, equipment, personnel, supplies, time, and so on. Planning ensures that scarce resources are used appropriately and in such a way that organizational objectives are met. When well executed, strategic planning can lead to reduced duplication of effort across product/service lines, increased entrepreneurial thinking, and improved financial performance.

While the advantages of strategic planning can be significant, there is also a real cost to engage in a process of this magnitude. One of the most common criticisms of planning is that it allows for less time to be spent on current operations and/or crisis resolution. In this regard, the importance of planning is overwhelmed and lost in day-to-day activities. Another perspective recognizes that the healthcare environment is changing rapidly—so fast, in fact, that plans and objectives are obsolete by the time they are developed and implemented. Both of these positions consider planning to be a waste of scarce resources, as the planning process itself requires resources.

Another challenge to planning in healthcare organizations is the ability to identify the customer. Identifying your customers and focusing on their needs is a basic tenet of any business. However, in healthcare, the customer depends on the perspective taken. Many would say that the patient is the customer, and from the care perspective that is indeed the case. But from the financial perspective, the payer (e.g., Medicare, Medicaid, private insurance) is the customer. Other views maintain that the customer is the employer, the government, or society as a whole. Developing strategies that take into consideration a variety of different customers can be considered impossible when there are competing priorities and requirements necessary to meet customer needs.

Finally, an organization can face barriers to planning from management and staff. Administrators who are not trained in the planning process and/or who do not have experience with planning are less likely to value and engage in planning activities. Professionals (e.g., physicians, nurses) may have goals driven by their professions that conflict with organizational goals. And implementing plans can be fraught with problems that management and staff are not equipped to handle.

So, do the advantages of strategic planning outweigh the disadvantages? If you examine the commonly cited disadvantages, you often see the solution to those challenges is actually a plan. Take, for example, the argument that time spent planning takes away from time spent on daily operations. Strategic planning assesses the internal and external environments, looking for ways to improve the effectiveness and efficiency of operations. If successful, more time in the future will be available for daily operating activities because less time will be spent reacting to changing market conditions (at least those that were predictable). Maybe a story can help drive home the point.

Two men, one older and one younger, were logging and decided to have a contest—the man who felled the most trees that day would win. Both men grabbed an axe and headed for the forest. The younger man went to work at a furious pace, chopping down tree after tree. On several occasions during the day he noticed the older man walking back to the truck for a rest, and snickered to himself how fun it was going to be gloating about his win. He worked hard all day, never taking a break. But at the end of the day, the tree count of the older man was nearly double that of the younger man. "Incredible!" the younger man exclaimed. "How did you do that when I saw you resting several times today, and I never took a break?" The older man grinned and said, "I wasn't resting at all. I just took breaks to sharpen my axe when it became dull." The older man knew that the investment of time sharpening his axe would pay dividends, as a sharp axe chops more quickly and easily than a dull axe.

Abraham Lincoln once said, "Give me six hours to chop down a tree and I will spend the first four sharpening the axe." What President Lincoln knew was that time spent planning for success was instrumental in achieving success.

WE DON'T HAVE A PLAN FOR THIS

The best laid plans for mice and men often go awry.

—*Adapted from a line in* To a Mouse *by Robert Burns*
Scottish poet

The planning process involves a tremendous amount of time and effort, and requires continuous attention. The strategic planning process, described in Chapter 2, outlines the basic steps and notes some of the major resources required for successful development and implementation. The rewards are a focused road map toward organizational success that, when implemented, should guide the organization for the next few years. But sometimes life just does not cooperate.

THE CASE OF HURRICANE MARIA

On September 20, 2017 at 6:15 a.m., Puerto Rico was buffeted by a Category 4 hurricane with maximum sustained winds of 155 miles per hour. The results, magnified by the aftermath of Hurricane Irma that hit the island just 2 weeks before, moved beyond the definition of "disaster" and the event was termed "catastrophic." During the worst of the storm, some parts of the island were drenched with 30 inches of rain in a 24-hour period, the public power utility reported that its entire electrical infrastructure was destroyed, and both the airport and port were closed.

Now imagine that you are the manager of Castaner General Hospital, a 75-year-old small, rural hospital located in the mountains of west-central Puerto Rico. Because the hospital had, through its planning process, invested in infrastructure such as a certified well and a new electric generator (installed days before the storm hit), Castaner General is one of a handful of hospitals that have remained open and are functioning. A critical patient arrives and needs life-saving services that are

(*continued*)

(continued)

offered only at the tertiary care hospital in Ponce, about 35 miles away. The roads are blocked and eroded, and there is no way to communicate with the tertiary care hospital to let them know of the need. What do you do?

The head physician implements a communications contingency plan, an action plan that is prepared in the event that normal operations are impeded. The physician makes contact with the local police department and asks them to contact the station at the next town via radio. This process is completed from town to town, until a policeman near Ponce takes the request for transfer to each of the area tertiary care hospitals—law requires prior notice of patient transfer. Of the four hospitals in Ponce, two were operating and one agreed to accept the transfer.

The next problem to tackle is the inability of the ambulance to get to Ponce. An employee of Castaner General drives his four-wheel drive vehicle ahead of the ambulance, scouting for safe passage. Community members join the employee and use poles to remove downed power lines and debris blocking the route. Thankfully, the patient arrives at the referral hospital and receives the treatment he or she desperately needs.

Disasters are often associated with contingency plans; however, these plans have a much wider application. **Contingency plans** are "Plan B" plans designed to answer the question: What do we do if our normal operations are disrupted? And since interruptions to normal operations can and often do occur, developing contingency plans should be part of an organization's risk management process.

The process of developing contingency plans includes the following:

1. **Identify key risk areas**, reviewing operational areas to identify where things could go wrong. Getting input from employees and other stakeholders is important in this step. Examples of key areas include: disruptions due to natural disasters; succession planning for key personnel; response to a public relations crisis; loss of a key supplier.
2. **Prioritize risks** because one cannot feasibly plan for every contingency. Priorities should be determined based on the likelihood of the disruptive event and the magnitude of the effect on operations. A risk impact/probability chart can be used to help in prioritizing the impact on operations given the probability of occurrence of a specific event (see Figure 1.5). Operational areas that fall in the upper right corner are considered critical and should have developed contingency plans. Management should assess the other operational areas in the other quadrants to determine the need for contingency plans.
3. **Create contingency plans** for each of the key areas identified, including timelines, personnel and other resource requirements, and communication.
4. **Maintain the contingency plans** to make sure that they are updated and available. For example, do not store contingency plans solely in electronic format in case there is a power outage.

FIGURE 1.5 Risk Impact/Probability Chart

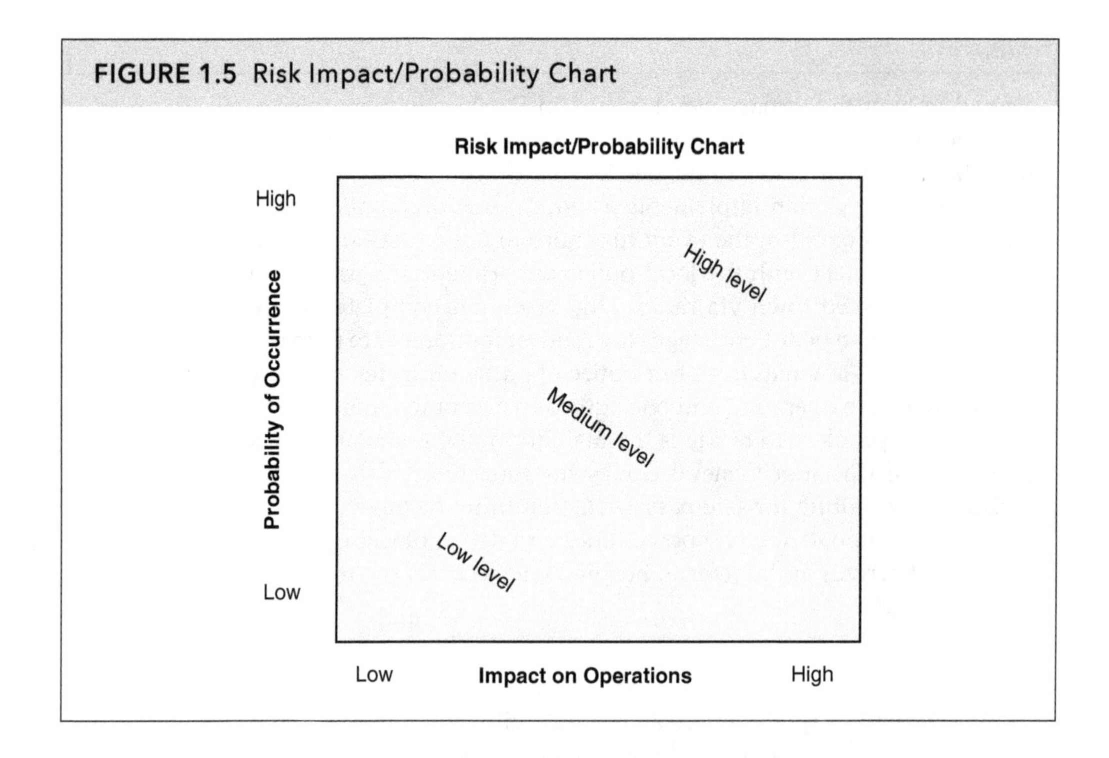

CASE STUDY MEMORIAL HOSPITAL, INC.

Fictitious Memorial Hospital is a **501(c)(3)** nonprofit, 500-bed, tertiary care, regional community teaching hospital with a Level 1 trauma center and a children's hospital. Established over 100 years ago as a community hospital, Memorial Hospital is centrally located in the state and provides about 415,000 patient visits annually.

The Memorial Hospital Board of Trustees was established through the County Code, with 13 trustees appointed by the governor upon recommendation of the County Council and two ex officio members appointed by the County Council. Terms are for 4 years and are staggered such that one-third of the members' terms expire every 4 years. The board has as its primary responsibilities hiring/firing of the CEO and fiduciary oversight of Memorial Hospital. The hospital CEO, chief financial officer (CFO), and in-house legal counsel attend all board meetings as nonvoting members.

Memorial Hospital serves as a referral hospital for residents across the state, and offers a full range of services under eight strategic service units (SSUs): cardiology, oncology, orthopedics, obstetrics/gynecology, neonatology, surgery (including robotic-assisted surgery), trauma, and behavioral health. The primary market area for Memorial Hospital consists of three counties, with a total population of 796,500. The secondary market for the hospital consists of 13 counties, with a total population of 678,000. With over 3,500 employees and

(continued)

CASE STUDY MEMORIAL HOSPITAL, INC. (*continued*)

a medical/dental staff of 750, Memorial Hospital provides a wide range of primary and specialty care services.

Most of the medical staff of Memorial Hospital are not employees of the hospital, and there has historically been a stressed relationship between the medical staff and hospital administration. In the fee-for-service system, physician and hospital incentives are often opposed, particularly in the inpatient market. Patient length of stay and excessive test ordering have been particular areas of concern for the CEO and board; however, physicians have been reluctant to receive the hospital's messages on the impact on reimbursement. Recently, the hospital has been developing an ACO with physicians and other partners, and this activity has increased communication and collaboration during the past 3 years. Over 90% of the medical staff have admitting privileges at other local hospitals.

The population in Memorial Hospital's primary and secondary service areas has been growing steadily at about 1.25% per year. Median household income at the last census was $48,250, 15% of the population is living in poverty, and 14% of the population is below 100% of the federal poverty level. Approximately two-thirds (67%) of the population is White, 28% Black, 2.5% Hispanic or Latino, 2% Asian, and 0.5% American Indian or Alaska Native. The unemployment rate has held steady at 4.1%, mirroring the national average, and has been declining since reaching 10% 5 years ago.

Memorial Hospital reported $27 million in net income on its last audited Statement of Operations (income statement). As a referral center and teaching hospital providing high-intensity medical services, Memorial Hospital patient-care expenses were one of the highest in the state and its average length of stay was almost 50% higher than that of competitors and of norms. Memorial Hospital receives significant revenue through donations, the provision of non–patient-care services, and investment income.

Memorial Hospital has three local competitors—one private hospital, one faith-based nonprofit hospital, and one county hospital. Each of these competitors is within a 60-mile radius of Memorial Hospital. While the market is competitive, Memorial Hospital has been able to maintain 45% overall market share in its 16-county primary and secondary market. Memorial Hospital works hard to increase its private pay market share, where it sees its largest profit margins. Memorial Hospital's payer mix (all services) is:

- 42.0% Medicare
- 20.5% Medicaid
- 29.0% private insurance
- 8.5% self-pay/uninsured

There is also a Department of Veterans Affairs (VA) hospital in the market, and Memorial Hospital provides some services to eligible beneficiaries through contracts for noncompetitive services.

GLOSSARY OF TERMS

501(c)(3) status—a nonprofit designation of tax exemption bestowed by the Internal Revenue Service (IRS) to organizations that are incorporated and operated exclusively for exempt purposes set forth in section 501(c)(3) of the Internal Revenue Code, that do not inure any earnings to private shareholders or individuals, and are not an action organization (i.e., may not attempt to influence legislation as a substantial part of activities and may not participate in any campaign activity for or against political candidates)

Board—a governing body that establishes policies for management and makes major decisions that affect the organization

Board of Directors—a group of individuals elected to represent stockholders/owners in a for-profit organization

Board of Trustees—a group of individuals appointed or elected to represent stakeholders in a nonprofit organization

CEO—the highest ranking executive within the organization, responsible for managing the organization and carrying out the direction of the board

Contingency plan—a plan that is implemented when normal operations are disrupted or normal plans fail

Controlling—a managerial function in which feedback is used to ensure that organizational objectives are being addressed and met as planned

Directing—a managerial function that deals with human resources from a motivation and communication perspective

External assessment—an evaluation of the uncontrollable variables residing outside of the organization

Internal assessment—an evaluation of the controllable variables residing inside of the organization

Long-term planning—the process of developing plans over a longer period of time (typically more than 3 years) by extrapolating information known today

Organizing—a managerial function for unifying scarce resources within the organization to complete the objectives identified in the plan

Operational plans—plans written to cover activities expected to occur within a 12-month period

Planning—a managerial function concerned with creating a detailed blueprint that, when implemented, is meant to achieve specific organizational objectives

Staffing—a managerial function that specifically addresses the human resource component and the relationship to planned objectives

Strategic plans—plans written to cover a longer period of time, typically 5 years or less

Tactical plans—plans written to cover a mid-length period of time, typically 1 to 2 years or less

REFERENCES

Bracker, J. (1980). The historical development of the strategic management concept. *Academy of Management Review*, *5*(2), 219–224. doi:10.5465/amr.1980.4288731

Centers for Medicare & Medicaid Services. (2018). NHE fact sheet. Retrieved from https://www.cms.gov/research-statistics-data-and-systems/statistics-trends-and-reports/nationalhealthexpenddata/nhe-fact-sheet.html

Koontz, H., & O'Donnell, C. (1976). *Management: A systems and contingency analysis of managerial functions.* New York, NY: McGraw-Hill.

Simyar, F., Lloyd-Jones, J., & Caro, J. (1988). Strategic management: A proposed framework for the health care industry. In F. Simyar & J. Lloyd-Jones (Eds.), *Strategic management in the health care sector: Toward the year 2000* (pp. 6–17). Englewood Cliffs, NJ: Prentice Hall.

Sun Tzu & Griffith, S. B. (1964). *The art of war*. Oxford, United Kingdom: Clarendon Press.

CHAPTER 2

THE STRATEGIC PLANNING PROCESS

The best way to predict the future is to create it.

—Peter Drucker
Management consultant and author

LEARNING OBJECTIVES

1. Describe the fundamental steps in a good strategic planning process.
2. Discuss the importance of good leadership.
3. Identify the sources of power.
4. Differentiate between leadership styles.
5. Discuss the impact of quality improvement processes in strategic planning.

Kristi sat in her kitchen with her head in her hands. "Where did I go wrong?," she asked herself. She had always been told that her oatmeal chocolate-chip cookies were so scrumptious that she could make a fortune selling them. When she decided to invest the time and money to make and market her cookies, she considered the cost of the ingredients and packaging, her time, and even a small amount for distribution. While some potential customers indicated that they were not interested because the cookies were pricey, Kristi had no problem selling her product and taking new orders.

Business had been so good for the first two months that Kristi had considered hiring someone to manage the sales while she concentrated on baking. Then the floor fell out from under her! People just did not seem as interested in her cookies anymore. A friend suggested that she conduct marketing activities that would elicit potential customers' opinions of her cookies, packaging, and pricing. What Kristi found was that people really did enjoy her cookies, but that the alternatives from grocery stores and other bakeries provided similar quality at much lower prices. It is not that Kristi had ignored the fact that there was a lot of competition in the cookie market, it was that she believed her cookies would be different. "How could I have been so naive?"

■ ■ ■

THE FLOW OF THE STRATEGIC PLANNING PROCESS

> "Cheshire Cat," Alice began . . . "Would you please tell me which way I ought to go from here?" "That depends on where you want to get to," said the cat.
>
> —*Lewis Carroll*
> *Alice in Wonderland*

Kristi's cookie business would have benefited from completing each of the steps in the strategic planning process. We saw in Chapter 1 that Simyar and colleagues identified an ordered sequence for healthcare strategic planning (Simyar, Lloyd-Jones, & Caro, 1988):

- Identify the organization's current position, including present **mission**, long-term objectives, **strategies**, and policies.
- Analyze the environment.
- Conduct an organizational audit.
- Identify the various alternative strategies based on relevant data.
- Select the best alternative.
- Gain acceptance.
- Prepare long- and short-range plans to support and carry out the strategy.
- Implement the plan and conduct ongoing evaluation.

Essentially, the strategic planning process seeks to answer three fundamental questions:

1. What will we do?
   - What *specific* needs does the organization want to meet?
2. Why/for whom will we do it?
   - Which groups have needs that we want to meet?
3. How will we do what we want to do?
   - Of the many different possible ways to accomplish something, how will we do it?

There is tension between being innovative by moving away from a tried-and-true business model and being complacent and risking becoming outdated. One purpose of the strategic planning process is to ensure that the organization is continuously considering these fundamental questions in such

FIGURE 2.1 The Strategic Planning Process

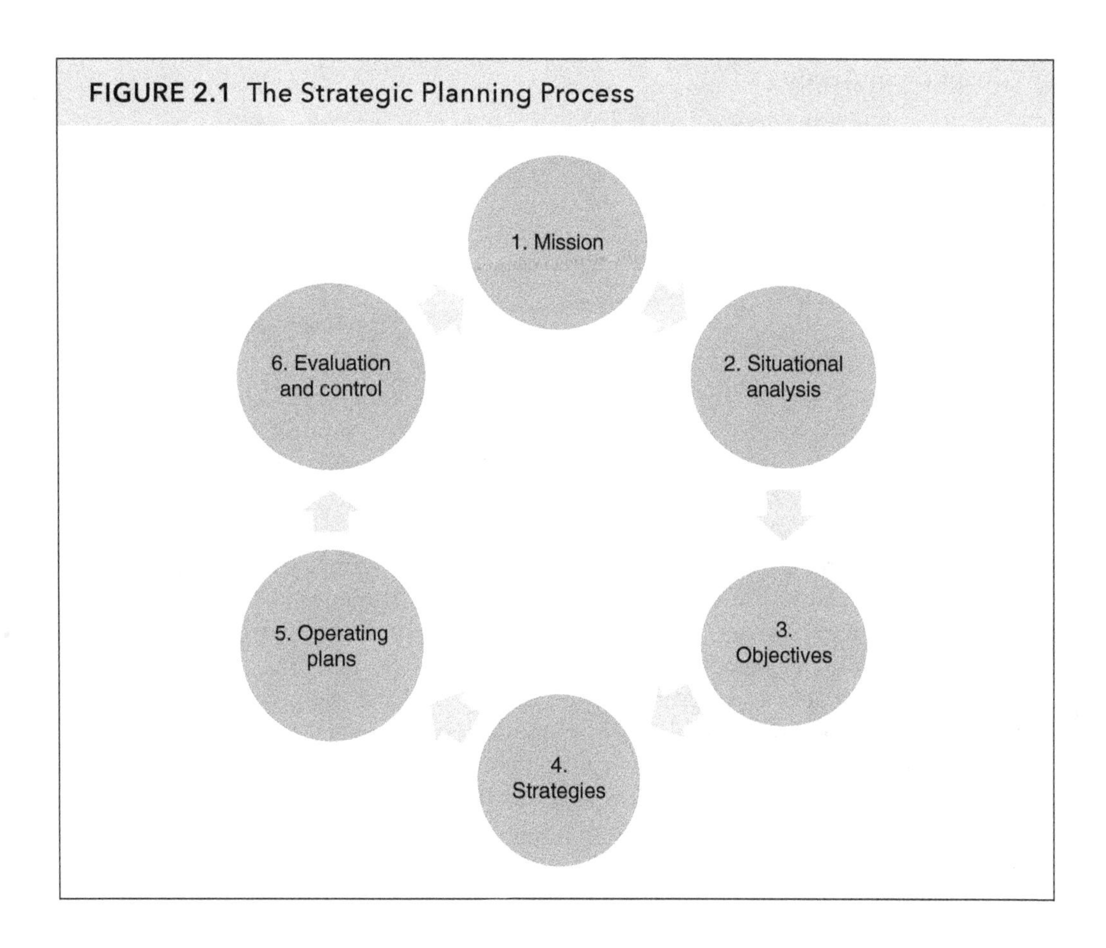

a way that the organization can adapt to changing circumstances over time. Graphically, the strategic planning process can be portrayed as six activities that happen in a specific order (Figure 2.1).

1. Mission

Every organization has a purpose—when the organization was founded, it was founded for some reason. For example, a desire by civic leaders in a community to improve the health status of people in their region could lead to a grassroots effort to build a medical school. In that case, the purpose of the medical school would be to improve the health status of residents in the area by providing a highly trained, skilled physician workforce. And every objective, strategy, and operating plan would be written to meet that organizational purpose. As Calvin Coolidge, president of the United States (1923–1929), said: "No enterprise can exist for itself alone. It ministers to some need, it performs some great service not for itself but for others; or failing therein it ceases to be profitable and ceases to exist."

It is difficult to plan for the future if you do not have a firm grip of where you stand in the present. The mission statement provides that grounding. A more detailed discussion of organizational purpose is found in Chapter 3.

2. Situational Analysis

> If you think what exists today is permanent and forever true, you inevitably get your head handed to you.
>
> —*John Reed*
> *Former chairman, Citicorp/Citibank/Citigroup*

The uncertainty of the future is certain. The environment within which organizations operate, and the organizations themselves, will change. And change is accelerating and significant. These statements can make a healthcare manager lose sleep at night, but they also point to the importance of assessing the internal and external environments. Planning takes the position that anything that can happen probably will happen, so it is best to be prepared for change.

The first step in preparing is to assess the organization itself through an internal audit. The audit is conducted at the corporate level and for each service line or business unit, so that the strengths and weaknesses of the organization can be objectively identified.

Being able to manage change means that we must constantly monitor the environment in which we operate—hence the need to assess the external environment. What are the expected reimbursement trends? What changes in governmental regulations are likely to affect our business? Do we expect new competitive entrants into the market? What is happening with interest rates, and what effect will that have on capital projects? How are the demographics of our market area changing? Is the supply/demand of the health workforce changing significantly? Which new technologies will drive healthcare utilization in the foreseeable future? These and other questions should be explored to determine the impact that the environment will have on the operations of our organization. The goal is to identify trends and update our overview of the environment in which we operate.

The purpose of internal and external assessment is to identify internal strengths that can be matched to opportunities identified in the market, and internal weaknesses that can be minimized to reduce environmental threats. A common method used to conduct a **situational analysis**, or environmental assessment, is a strengths, weaknesses, opportunities, and threats (**SWOT**) analysis, which we discuss in Chapter 4.

3. Objectives

> It must be borne in mind that the tragedy of life does not lie in not reaching your goal. The tragedy of life lies in having no goal to reach.
>
> —*Benjamin Elijah Mays*
> *American civil rights leader and activist*

Once the internal and external environments have been assessed and the organization's mission has been considered, the next step is to begin to outline the future direction for the organization. **Objectives** (aka, **"goals," "targets,"** and **"key results"**) are clear, concise, measurable, written statements that identify what is to be accomplished, and by whom, over a period of time. They convey the long-term strategic direction that moves the organization toward meeting its mission. In fact, management believes that these objectives must be met in order for the organization to achieve its purpose. Objectives answer the question Where do we want to go? and provide standards against which to measure results. Objectives are also identified to leverage any competitive advantages an organization might have against its competitors. Objectives are discussed further in Chapter 5.

4. Strategies

> Hope is not a strategy.
>
> —*U.S. Air Force Special Operations pilot*

If objectives answer the question Where do we want to go? then strategies answer the question How do we get there? There are usually many ways to accomplish each objective, and all potential options should be evaluated. The final strategies can be thought of as activities that need to be accomplished to achieve the objectives—in essence, selected strategies become the link between objectives and results. In Chapter 6, we explore how strategies are selected.

5. Operating Plans

> Someone's sitting in the shade today because someone planted a tree a long time ago.
>
> —*Warren Buffett*
> *Businessman, investor, and philanthropist*

Operating plans (aka, **action plans**) are the mechanisms through which individual strategies are implemented. They identify who within the organization needs to do what with which resources in order for the strategy to be successful. As such, they are infused within the organization across all levels and operational areas. Realizing strategies through operating plans is discussed further in Chapter 6.

6. Evaluation and Control

> One of the great mistakes is to judge policies and programs by their intentions rather than their results.
>
> —*Milton Friedman*
> *American economist*

It is possible for an organization to complete each of the previous steps in the strategic planning process and still fail to move toward its purpose. The reason is the same reason why planning is so important—things change. Recognizing this reality, **evaluation and control** should be a natural progression of the strategic plan so that modifications and adjustments can be made.

Once the plan is implemented, results are produced. These results should be compared to the associated objectives to evaluate performance and identify areas where adjustment should be made. The base of this evaluation occurs in the individual performance appraisal, where personnel know what is expected of them and are rewarded for their contributions. If each employee in the organization completes his or her job tasks, and those tasks are tied to the objectives identified in the strategic plan, then the plan will be accomplished. The process of evaluation and control is discussed in Chapter 7.

THE IMPORTANCE OF GOOD LEADERSHIP

Good leadership is a foundational requirement for an organization in any industry to be efficient and effective. Leadership is so important to the strategic planning process that a brief discussion is warranted. Further study of leadership through a course, text, and/or independent reading is highly recommended. As we learned in Chapter 1, healthcare organizations operate in a dynamic environment. In addition to rapid change, leaders are pressured to reduce costs, improve clinical outcomes, and maintain high levels of patient satisfaction. As a result, today's healthcare organizations need leaders who can motivate employees toward a common purpose and, in the framework of strategic planning, set the organization's course for the future.

The concept of leadership has been studied and written about extensively. Warren G. Bennis, an expert on leadership, said that "Leadership is the capacity to translate vision into reality." The single largest resource that leaders in the healthcare industry have is the human resource (personnel), since healthcare is largely a service industry. Managers, who are responsible for performance outcomes, must leverage personnel and other resources to maximize efficiency and effectiveness. Moving down the road from vision to reality requires the ability to motivate, to inspire, and to engage others in such a way that they want to follow the leader's direction.

Getting others to do what you want them to do is often thought of within the context of power—the degree of authority and influence over others. Sociologists John French and Bertram Raven wrote in 1959 that there are five bases of power that may be exerted to influence others, and that the potential for such influence was a result of social power (French & Raven, 1959). **Legitimate power (**aka, **positional power)** is commonly recognized because it is founded in the formal position the person holds in an organization. The vice president of women's and children's services in a hospital is expected to have a tremendous amount of power over those persons who work in that strategic business unit. The legitimacy of this power can be verified through the organizational chart and job description. **Expert power** is derived from knowledge, and those with such knowledge are often held in high esteem by other employees. As a result, employees are influenced by those with expert power. Expert power is often the precursor to legitimate power but may also be held by an employee who does not have managerial authority. For example, a data analyst may hold expert power because he or she knows how to manipulate the data, which can skew the balance of power with a manager who does not have that skillset.

When someone is respected and liked within an organization, that person has a degree of **referent power**. People with referent power are described as charismatic, and the influence they have over others is based on admiration. The last two types of power are based on positive and negative reinforcement. **Coercive power** is the ability of an individual to punish, and therefore to influence others who try to avoid the punishment (e.g., being fired or reprimanded). On the positive side, someone with **reward power** can influence others by offering incentives (e.g., a bonus or promotion).

In practice, a manager has legitimate power (at least within his or her unit) and likely holds expert power. The ability to coerce and reward is typically part of legitimate power, although rewards may be limited to the ability of the organization to provide such incentives. In those cases, referent power can be a potent source of influence.

The way in which a manager interacts with employees is often referred to as **leadership style**. Practice dictates using different styles, or combinations of styles, in a given situation. Psychologist Kurt Lewin developed a framework of three leadership styles during the 1930s (Lewin, Lippitt, & White, 1939). **Autocratic leadership** involves close supervision of the employee by the leader, who tells the employee what will be done and how. This style is most effective when there is a clear chain of command, and it is understood that the leader holds legitimate power. While this style of leadership gets results, the lack of room for employee creativity and initiative typically makes this style the least effective in motivating employees over a long period of time.

Democratic leadership style encourages creativity and participation of individuals and teams in decision making. While the leader makes the final decision, team members feel included and typically have high job satisfaction and productivity. This style does not lend itself well to situations in which quick decisions need to be made. When leaders give their employees the freedom to determine how best to accomplish tasks, and the ability to set deadlines to meet those tasks, they are using the **laissez-faire ("free reign") style of leadership**. This is a hands-off approach to managing, where the leader supports the activities of the employees and is available for consultation and advice but is otherwise uninvolved. The lack of supervision can lead to disorganization and catastrophic results and is typically not used as an independent style on a consistent basis.

A more recent managerial concept is **transformational leadership**, in which leaders focus on linking their goals and values with their employees by developing a common purpose (Sullivan & Decker, 2000). When successful, leaders become motivational and employees become confident and loyal, internalizing the leader's values and convictions. Transformational leadership is grounded in the work of a psychologist who is familiar to any student

FIGURE 2.2 Maslow's Hierarchy of Needs

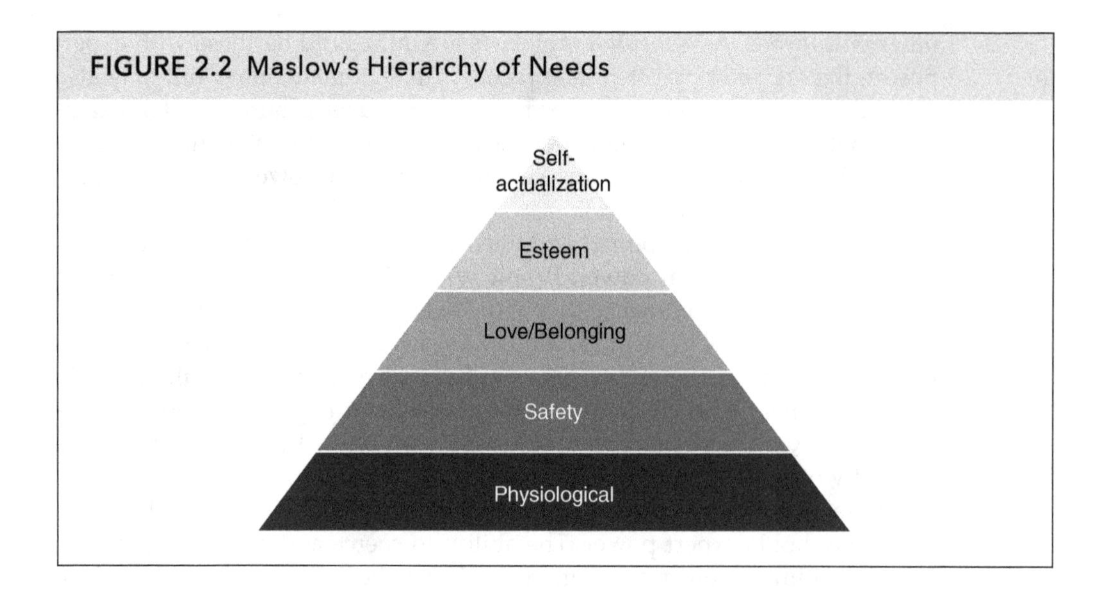

who has studied motivation—Abraham Maslow. Maslow's famous Hierarchy of Needs (Maslow, 1943)—see Figure 2.2—distinguishes different levels of human needs that must be satisfied in a particular order, with a requirement that lower level needs (i.e., physiological needs) must be met before the individual can move to the next level (i.e., safety and security).

Transformational leadership incorporates self-esteem and self-actualization by:

1. Making employees aware that the tasks they complete are important
2. Empowering employees to promote change
3. Encouraging employees to think and act to meet organizational goals
4. Creating an environment of team-based decision making for improved organizational performance

In the realm of strategic planning, where setting a purpose and a road to achieve that purpose is paramount, transformational leadership can be a powerful motivator. However, in practice, managers will apply leadership styles based on circumstances.

STRATEGIC PLANNING AS AN ONGOING PROCESS

Strategic planning should not be a one-time event. Rather, it is an ongoing process. Figure 2.1 shows this clearly in that the process is circular and continuous, which requires strategic thinking on a daily basis. We use the information we gain through the evaluation and control step to ask questions about our progress. Are we advancing toward achieving our objectives and, therefore, our mission? Is the strategy that we selected working? Do we need to shift resources from one action item to another? These are the types of questions that leaders need to ask, so that the assumptions that were made in developing the plan do not paralyze the organization when those assumptions are violated.

Strategic planning is a process. While there are many strategic planning formats from which to choose, each is a road map that guides the organization to its chosen destination over a significant period of time. And just like when driving on a long trip, the organization sees versions of highway signs, mile markers, attractions, and accidents along the way. Such feedback can be positive or negative and can result in the need for major or minor edits to the strategic plan. As a result, strategic plans are often described as "living" or "breathing" documents. The healthcare industry moves too quickly for any organization to create a 3- to 5-year plan and then do nothing until the next planning cycle.

Since strategic planning is a process, it can be studied and improved. This allows the organization to react to internal and external changes in such a way that the organization can benefit. In recognizing that a process is composed of activities that are linked, a prudent organization will evaluate how changes in one area may impact other areas. Finally, recognizing strategic planning as a process with multiple components all working in concert with each other allows stakeholders (including employees) to see the role they play in helping the organization achieve its purpose, a powerful motivation.

In addition to continuous feedback and evaluation, the strategic plan itself should be updated at regular intervals. If the plan is written for a 3-year period of time, then the next iteration of planning should result in an updated or new plan in year 4. In addition to the current plan expiring, there are other circumstances that would indicate that an update is prudent, such as:

- Substantial changes to the competitive environment
- Major shifts in the funding environment
- Important changes to organizational leadership
- Significant fluctuations in regulations and policies

PLAN-DO-STUDY-ACT (PDSA) AND CONTINUOUS QUALITY IMPROVEMENT

Strategic planning efforts often include quality improvement activities, which help the organization plan, implement, and monitor evidence-based changes. In 2012, the Institute for Healthcare Improvement (IHI, n.d.) developed the **Triple Aim**, a framework for optimizing health system performance. Achieving the Triple Aim of healthcare—improving the patient experience of care, improving the health of populations, and reducing the per capita cost of healthcare—drives organizations to expand improvement efforts. Quality improvement activities give staff confidence in responding to needs and in

FIGURE 2.3 The Plan-Do-Study-Act (PDSA) Model

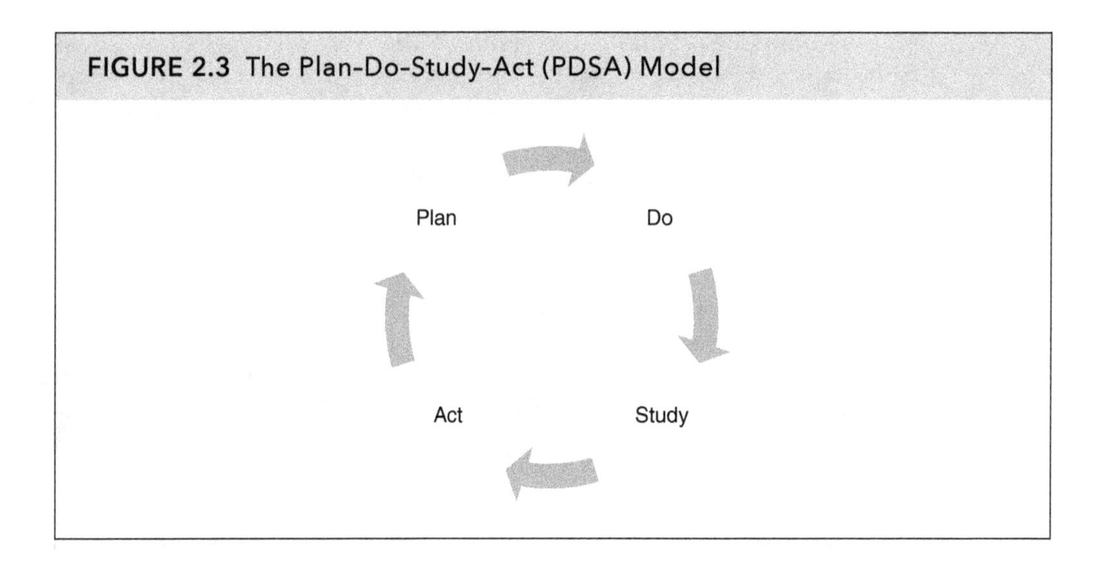

determining whether or not they are improving the situation. Continuous quality improvement is a structured approach that encourages the questions: How are we doing? and How can we do better?

One model for quality improvement is the **PDSA** cycle, a four-step problem-solving process used by businesses as part of continuous quality improvement efforts (see Figure 2.3). PDSA, also known as PDCA (plan–do–check–act), Deming cycle, Shewhart cycle, and Deming wheel, can be used in conjunction with other quality initiatives, such as Six Sigma and Lean.

PDSA steps include planning an intervention (**plan**), pilot testing the change on a small scale (**do**), observing and measuring the result of the change (**study**), and using knowledge gained to plan for the next steps (**act**). Improvement projects can be addressed across a spectrum: single unit, multiple unit, identified population, or community. For example, a hospital might implement a quality improvement project to address bed sores on a surgical unit, address hospital-acquired infections across multiple units, influence the utilization of the emergency department (ED) by asthmatic children, or participate in public health activities in a partnership of health and human services providers.

Quality improvement initiatives should be driven by the corporate strategies outlined in the strategic plan. The IHI suggests a Model for Improvement developed by Associates in Process Improvement (n.d.) as a tool to accelerate improvement. The model (Figure 2.4) assumes any changes that are driven by the strategic planning assumptions and incorporates the PDSA cycle.

Any continuous quality improvement process relies on data, and it is important to ensure that data are timely, accurate, and representative of what they were intended to measure. Once the process is complete, it is important that comparative data are available in the form of baseline data and national or regional benchmarks, so that the organization can relate how well it is doing relative to itself and others in the industry.

FIGURE 2.4 Associates in Process Improvement

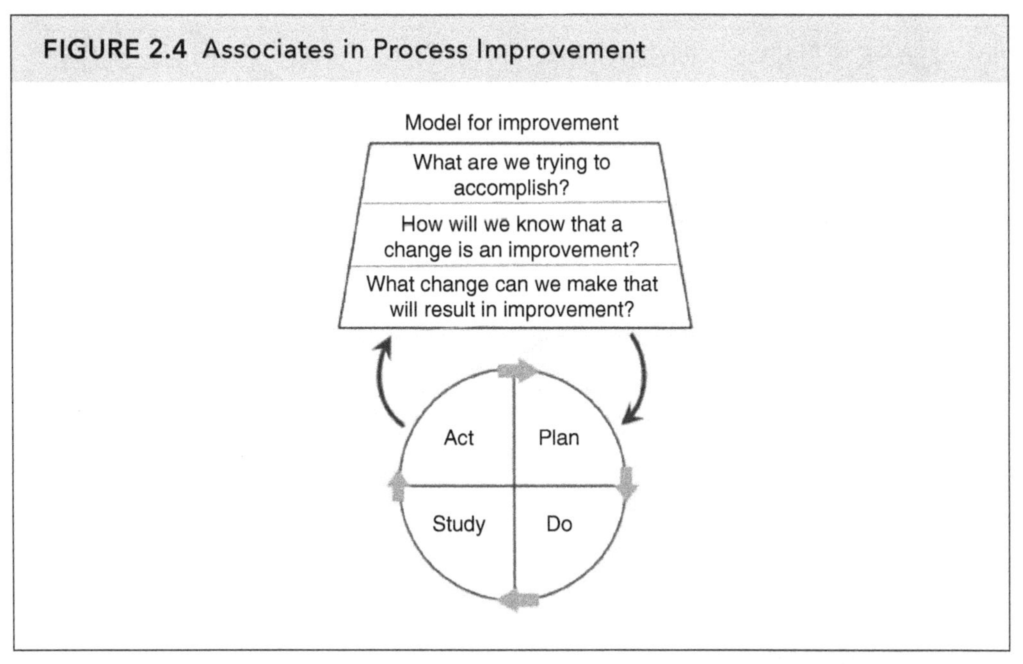

Source: The Institute for Healthcare Improvement suggests a Model for Improvement developed by Associates in Process Improvement (http://www.apiweb.org) as a tool to accelerate improvement. The model (Figure 2.4) assumes any changes that are driven by the strategic planning assumptions and incorporates the PDSA Cycle.

CASE STUDY MEMORIAL HOSPITAL, INC.

Memorial Hospital has conducted strategic planning since the early 1970s. Initially, these plans covered a 10-year period; however, more recently, the hospital has moved from a 5-year to a 3-year planning cycle. Updates to the strategic plan are provided by the executive management team at the annual board retreat. These updates are based on ongoing monitoring and reporting of strategic activities through the Department of Planning and Marketing.

Memorial Hospital is in its second year of the current 3-year cycle, and the chief executive officer (CEO) has tasked the director of planning and marketing with overseeing development of the new plan. The CEO has made a public announcement to employees and select external stakeholders about the upcoming process, and the director of planning and marketing has selected a strategic planning committee comprising mid- and upper-level management.

The strategic planning committee is responsible for:

1. Evaluating the mission, vision, and values of Memorial Hospital, including input from a broad spectrum of stakeholders (e.g., employees, community partners, board members, donors)
2. Conducting an environmental assessment and suggesting objectives and strategies to the CEO

(*continued*)

CASE STUDY MEMORIAL HOSPITAL, INC. (*continued*)

3. Coordinating planning activities at different levels within the hospital
4. Providing planning expertise and resources to managers in the hospital who will be tasked with planning activities

The CEO has directed the chief financial officer (CFO) to set aside funding to support these activities.

Developing a full-blown strategic plan requires time and resources that are beyond the scope of a course; however, students can gain valuable experience developing a quasi-strategic plan. In order to facilitate a "real-world" learning experience, a series of worksheets are included at the end of several chapters. The following planning process worksheet includes several questions to encourage you to think about the strategic planning process and how it would be implemented within an organization.

PLANNING PROCESS WORKSHEET

1. Who should be involved in the planning process?

____

____

____

____

2. Where will planning sessions be held?

____

____

____

____

3. When will planning sessions be held?

____

____

____

____

4. What types of background material do participants need prior to starting the first session?

____

____

5. Who will lead the process? Who will ultimately be responsible for arranging sessions and getting materials distributed?

6. When and how will the staff, board, employees, or others be involved in the process? How will feedback be collected?

7. How will the results be communicated to everyone in the organization?

8. Who will train/supervise managers in working with their own staff and in setting objectives, developing action plans, and conducting performance appraisals?

9. How frequently will the process be reviewed and by whom?

10. Who will be responsible for dealing with external groups (revenue sources, independent healthcare professionals, media consultants) in preparing the plan?

____

____

____

GLOSSARY OF TERMS

Autocratic leadership style—a style of leadership in which the manager believes that employees should be closely supervised and directed

Coercive power—power based on the ability of an individual to punish, and therefore to influence others who try to avoid the punishment (e.g., being fired or reprimanded)

Democratic leadership style—a style of leadership in which the manager encourages creativity and participation of employees in decision making

Evaluation and control—monitoring progress toward completion of objectives and making adjustments as needed

Expert power—power derived from knowledge

Laissez-faire ("free reign") leadership—a style of leadership in which the manager believes that employees should be free to determine the best way to accomplish tasks

Leadership style—the way a manager interacts with employees

Legitimate power (aka, **positional power**)—power that is founded in the formal position a person holds in an organization

Mission—an organization's purpose or reason for being

Objectives (aka, **goals, targets,** and **key results**)—clear, concise, measurable, written statements that identify what is to be accomplished, and by whom, over a period of time

Operating plans (aka, **action plans**)—mechanisms through which individual strategies are implemented

PDSA—a four-step problem-solving process (plan–do–study–act) used by businesses as part of continuous quality improvement efforts

Referent power—power that results from being respected and liked

Reward power—power based on the ability of an individual to reward others

Situational analysis—an assessment of the organization and the environment in which it operates

Strategies—activities that need to be accomplished to achieve objectives

SWOT—a situational analysis method that assesses an organization's strengths and weaknesses, and the external environment's opportunities and threats

Transformational leadership—a style of leadership in which the manager links goals and values with employees by developing common purpose

Triple Aim—a framework for optimizing health system performance, which includes improving the patient experience of care, improving the health of populations, and reducing the per capita cost of healthcare.

REFERENCES

Associates in Process Improvement. (n.d.). Model for improvement. Retrieved from http://www.apiweb.org

French, J. R. P., Jr., & Raven, B. H. (1959). The bases of social power. In D. Cartwright (Ed.), *Studies in social power* (pp. 150–167). Ann Arbor, MI: Institute for Social Research.

Institute for Healthcare Improvement. (n.d.). The IHI triple aim. Retrieved from http://www.ihi.org/Engage/Initiatives/TripleAim/Pages/default.aspx

Lewin, K., Lippitt, R., & White, R. K. (1939). Patterns of aggressive behavior in experimentally created social climates. *Journal of Social Psychology, 10,* 269–299. doi:10.1080/00224545.1939.9713366

Maslow, A. H. (1943). A theory of human motivation. *Psychological Review, 50*(4), 370–396. doi:10.1037/h0054346

Simyar, F., Lloyd-Jones, J., & Caro, J. (1988). Strategic management: A proposed framework for the health care industry. In F. Simyar & J. Lloyd-Jones (Eds.), *Strategic management in the health care sector: Toward the year 2000* (pp. 6–17). Englewood Cliffs, NJ: Prentice Hall.

Sullivan, E. J., & Decker, P. J. (2000). *Effective leadership and management in nursing*. Upper Saddle River, NJ: Prentice-Hall.

CHAPTER 3

ORGANIZATIONAL PURPOSE

Outstanding people have one thing in common: An absolute sense of mission.

—Hilary Hinton "Zig" Ziglar
Author, motivational speaker

LEARNING OBJECTIVES

1. Define what a mission statement is and how it is used by an organization.
2. Evaluate a mission statement.
3. Distinguish characteristics of a nonprofit versus for-profit organization.
4. Explain how the mission, vision, and values of an organization influence the activities included in the strategic plan.
5. Write a mission statement for a hypothetical organization.

For the past 15 years, Tom's nonprofit organization had helped to feed the homeless. The organization's simple mission statement read: "To provide a nutritious meal to those in need." What started as a soup kitchen in the basement of a local church feeding the needy in the community 3 days a week had become a commercial kitchen preparing and delivering daily meals at five sites across the city. The number of people served had ebbed and flowed with the economy, but there always seemed to be unmet needs. In fact, Tom's organization had been successful in securing donated new and gently used clothing and had been providing those free to families in need for the past 12 years. The success of his organization allowed Tom to pursue private grants to expand services 5 years ago. He added a staff member who provided financial counseling to help families get back on their feet and live within their means, and a social worker who could coordinate services that were offered by the city and state.

Two years ago, Tom was successful in securing a private foundation grant that was focused on transitional housing. The program allowed homeless clients who met income qualification to receive housing through contracts with an apartment facility and several hotels. A recent economic downturn resulted in high rates of unemployment, bankruptcies, and home foreclosures, and demand for transitional housing skyrocketed. Unfortunately, the poor economic climate had a negative impact on donations received by the nonprofit just at the time when service demands were at their highest. Tom found that he was drawing more and more money from the unrestricted fund to support the transitional housing needs—a practice that worried him because the feeding and clothing programs were supported from unrestricted funds. If the economic climate did not improve soon, or if additional grant funding was not realized, the core business of feeding the hungry would be jeopardized. Had the organization strayed too far from its mission?

■■■

THE MISSION STATEMENT

Basic Components of a Mission Statement

The purpose of an organization may be thought of as its reason for being. Why does it exist in the first place? This purpose is commonly referred to as its **mission** and is generally reported in a **mission statement**. Defining the mission of the organization, or validating that the mission is current, is the first step in the strategic planning process.

In order to maximize efficiency and effectiveness, organizations need to set clear and realistic objectives. A well-defined mission describes the needs to be met, sets the foundation for plans, strategies, and priorities, and acts as a sounding board for those activities. The mission also forms the basis for the organization's culture, and communicates the culture and intent of the organization both within and outside of the organization.

Writing a mission statement for a new organization, or significantly revising an existing mission statement, can be quite challenging. It requires a vision for what the organization should become, which should be approached with the participation of all relevant stakeholders. Words should be selected carefully, so that definitions of activities are not too vague to be meaningful and the organization does not engage in activities that are outside of its true purpose ("mission creep"). In this sense, the mission statement provides a boundary in which the organization makes decisions and operates.

The process of creating a mission statement should be a team effort. Since the mission statement will be used to convey information to a variety of people and organizations, a team made up of board members, executive leadership, employees (managers and nonmanagers), and external stakeholders should be assembled to describe the organization and its purpose. While mission statements vary across organizations and industries, most contain references to:

1. Identification of the market area served—Who are our customers and in which geographical area do they reside?
2. An effective description of the function of the business—What are the main products or services that we provide?
3. Organizational philosophy—What are our beliefs and values?

4. Strengths—What are our distinctive competencies?
5. Commitment to employees—How do we treat our employees?
6. Public image—Are we socially responsible and environmentally friendly?

The job of the team is to combine different perspectives and references to write one comprehensive statement. A benefit of using a varied team approach is that those who participate in the process are more likely to support the end result.

Effective mission statements are brief and memorable, so that internal and external stakeholders can remember the purpose of the organization and be able to explain that purpose to others. They should be inspirational and to the point. While mission statements are enduring and revisions are typically infrequent, management should periodically review and edit the statement if conditions warrant. New technologies, demographic trends, and consolidation within the industry are examples of reasons why an organization might want to review its current mission statement. The era of mergers and acquisitions in healthcare led to the need for many organizations to evaluate their mission statements. When, for example, a community-based nonprofit hospital was acquired by a for-profit hospital system, the mission of the acquired hospital was altered to reflect the mission of the parent organization and the role the newly acquired hospital played in the corporate structure.

Consider the mission statement for the National Aeronautics and Space Administration (NASA):

> Drive advances in science, technology, aeronautics, and space exploration to enhance knowledge, education, innovation, economic vitality, and stewardship of Earth.

What if NASA's mission had been "To send a human being on the moon"? On July 20, 1969, when Neil Armstrong and Edwin "Buzz" Aldrin walked on the moon, NASA would have fully satisfied its mission. Would the agency have celebrated its success and shut its doors? Its broader mission allows NASA to not only send someone to the moon, but also to engage in many other activities that "enhance knowledge, education, innovation, economic vitality, and stewardship of Earth."

Consider these other examples:

> To inspire hope, and contribute to health and well-being by providing the best care to every patient through integrated clinical practice, education and research.
>
> —*Mayo Clinic Health System*

> To ensure that the voices and needs of the populations we represent are present as the agency is developing, implementing, and evaluating its programs and policies.
>
> —*Centers for Medicare and Medicaid Services*

> The mission of Cleveland Clinic is to provide better care of the sick, investigation into their problems, and further education of those who serve.
>
> —*Cleveland Clinic*

Now, spend some time searching the Internet for mission statements of your favorite organizations. Be sure to include organizations both inside and outside the healthcare industry.

EVALUATING MISSION STATEMENTS

- How well do these mission statements meet the basic components we have identified?
- What changes would you recommend if you were chief executive officer (CEO)?

The Influence of Ownership

Mission statements for healthcare organizations (HCOs) may be influenced by their ownership status—nonprofit versus for-profit. Keep in mind that the mission statement denotes the organization's purpose or reason for being. Therefore, a mission typically reflects how an organization approaches markets, services, and financial goals.

Organizations that are incorporated and operated exclusively for exempt purposes set forth in section 501(c)(3) of the Internal Revenue Code, that do not inure any earnings to private shareholders or individuals, and are not an action organization may be considered tax-exempt by the Internal Revenue Service (IRS). These organizations are considered **nonprofit (aka, charitable organizations)**, are exempt from federal and property taxes, are exempt from federal taxation of interest paid on bonds, may write off bad debt as an expense, and may receive tax-deductible contributions. Historically, healthcare has been considered a charitable activity and organizations that meet the 501(c)(3) requirements have been granted that designation.

According to the American Hospital Association (AHA, 2018), the total number of registered hospitals in the United States was 5,534 in 2016. Ownership designation for these facilities is shown in Table 3.1.

Community hospitals are defined as nonfederal, short-term general, and other specialty hospitals. The vast majority of community hospitals in the United States are nongovernment (not-for-profit; Table 3.2). In 2016, 51.48% of all registered hospitals were nongovernment (not-for-profit).

The Affordable Care Act of 2010 imposed new requirements that *each* 501(c)(3) hospital facility must meet (IRS, n.d.):

1. Establish written financial assistance and emergency medical care policies.
2. Limit amounts charged for emergency or other medically necessary care to individuals eligible for assistance under the hospital's financial assistance policy.

TABLE 3.1 Registered Hospitals in the United States

Hospital Type	Number	Percentage
Community	4,840	87.49%
Federal	209	3.77%
Nonfederal psychiatric	397	7.17%
Nonfederal long-term care	78	1.40%
Institutions (prisons, colleges, etc.)	10	0.18%
TOTAL	5,534	100%

3. Make reasonable efforts to determine whether an individual is eligible for assistance under the hospital's financial assistance policy before engaging in extraordinary collection actions against the individual.
4. Conduct a community health needs assessments (CHNA) and adopt an implementation strategy at least once every 3 years.

Item 4, conducting a CHNA at least every 3 years, was a significant change to the tax-exempt requirements. The penalty for not meeting this requirement, an excise tax, impacted virtually all strategic plans in 501(c)(3)-designated hospital facilities.

For-profit organizations are owned by investors or shareholders, and their overarching purpose is to maximize shareholder wealth. This category includes organizations that are privately held with ownership by one or more individuals. For-profit organizations do not need to meet the requirements of nonprofit organizations and do not gain the benefits of that designation. They pay federal corporate taxes, state corporate income taxes, and local property taxes—amounts that can be significant. Contributions to for-profit corporations are not tax deductible and returns to investors are double-taxed (corporate taxes, then individual taxes). A major advantage that for-profit status offers is the ability to generate capital through the sale of stock.

TABLE 3.2 Community Hospitals in the United States

Community Hospital Status	Number	Percentage
Nongovernment (not-for-profit)	2,849	58.86%
Investor-owned (for-profit)	1,035	21.38%
State and local government	956	19.75%
TOTAL	4,840	100%

Benefits of a Well-Written Mission Statement

There are several organizational benefits to having a well-written mission statement (King, Case, & Premo, 2010; Williams, 2008). Included are:

1. Informing stakeholders, both within and outside the organization, of the organization's plans and goals
2. Uniting employees and others in a common purpose
3. Serving as a public relations tool
4. Providing a framework for allocation of resources
5. Indicating that the organization is proactive

Organizations serve a purpose to satisfy stakeholders, and that purpose must include focused activities in order to be successful. The mission statement provides an opportunity for the organization to present itself to current and future stakeholders, including customers, providers, suppliers, investors, donors, and employees. It provides information about the general direction of and what is important to the organization, as well as what the organization does not do/value. As a result, stakeholders understand the reason for growth, new products/services, and so on when they can see how these activities serve to carry out the corporate mission.

Importantly, organizations that take the time to craft a thoughtful, well-written mission statement are more likely to achieve their strategic plans and realize their purpose. But this outcome is highly dependent on the effort. If a mission statement is written, posted, and forgotten, success is not likely to be enhanced. However, if the mission statement is infused into the organization and permeates its culture, accountability is enhanced and the chance for success is increased.

Take, as an example, employee retention. Turnover is a huge expense for any organization, and particularly impactful in a service industry like healthcare. While employees may be motivated to leave an organization for an increase in pay, employees who are emotionally invested in the organization are less likely to leave for better compensation. A clear mission statement can unify employees, motivate and inspire, guide employee actions and decision making, and align efforts so that everyone is working toward the same goal.

Setting Vision for the Organization

> Strategic planning is worthless—unless there is first a strategic vision.
>
> —*John Naisbitt*
>
> *Author and speaker on futures studies*

An organization's mission statement can be thought of as its "current state." The **vision statement**, on the other hand, describes what the organization hopes to be in the future—its desired future state. In crafting a vision statement, organizational leaders and members envision an ideal future in the best possible world, and capture the conditions required for that world to exist. The vision is a long-term, lofty goal that inspires people and sets the tone for higher achievement within the organization. It is also less detailed than the mission, which outlines how the organization will go about achieving its vision. Vision statements are generally inspirational, clear, and memorable. They range in length from a few words to several sentences, although most tend to be brief.

The purpose of pursuing the mission is to see the vision become reality. Consider the Alzheimer's Association, the global leader in Alzheimer's advocacy, research, and support. Its mission is "To eliminate Alzheimer's disease through the advancement of research; to provide and enhance care and support for all affected; and to reduce the risk of dementia through the promotion of brain research." The vision of the Alzheimer's Association is "A world without Alzheimer's disease." The mission indicates why the organization exists, and the vision indicates the future it would like to see.

MISSION AND VISION EXAMPLE

In 2014, Rochester General Hospital and Unity Health System joined to form Rochester Regional Health. The mission of this new organization is "To enhance lives and preserve health by enabling access to a comprehensive, fully integrated network of the highest quality and most affordable care, delivered with kindness, integrity and respect." Rochester Regional Health's vision is "To lead the evolution of healthcare to enable every member of the communities we serve to enjoy a better, healthier life." The mission focuses on preserving health, and the vision looks to a time of health for all. (Courtesy Rochester Regional Health)

The Role of Organizational Values

Organizational values provide guidelines for beliefs, attitudes, and behaviors—they are the principles that bind the organization. Many organizations publish values along with their mission and vision statements as ethical standards framing how the organization will make decisions. Stated values typically express issues such as honesty and integrity, how patients will be treated, zero tolerance of illegal activities, and commitment toward employee development.

Values are also found implicitly in the organization's culture, providing guidance when employees make decisions. As job vacancies become available, the organization should seek candidates whose personal values match those of the organization. Similarly, applicants will likely be more satisfied working in an organization whose values are like their own.

VALUES EXAMPLE

Alton Memorial Hospital is a full-service hospital serving southwestern Illinois. Its values tell stakeholders that the hospital is patient-focused; disciplined (good stewards of the community's assets); and knowledge-driven. Additionally, the hospital demonstrates trust, dignity, and respect; high ethical standards and behaviors; and teamwork and accountability. These ideals convey to those outside of the hospital what to expect from interactions with hospital employees and tell hospital employees what is expected of their actions.

The Relationship of Mission, Vision, and Values

As you may have surmised, the mission, vision, and values of an organization are interrelated. The mission—the purpose or reason for being—is what the organization means to be today. The vision is what it aspires to stretch to be in a distant future. And the values are the guiding principles that set the culture within which the organization operates. These relationships are shown in Figure 3.1.

In Figure 3.1, the "M" represents the organization's mission—its purpose or reason for being. The "V" represents the organization's vision, or where it wants to be in some distant future. You can see that the vision broadens beyond the current mission. The dashed lines represent the organization's values, which act as boundaries within which the organization operates.

Straying From the Mission

There is a balance between working within the mission of the organization and the need to alter the mission to meet changing needs. If not vigilant, organizations can experience **mission creep** and shift focus to a purpose that is

FIGURE 3.1 The Relationship of Mission, Vision, and Values

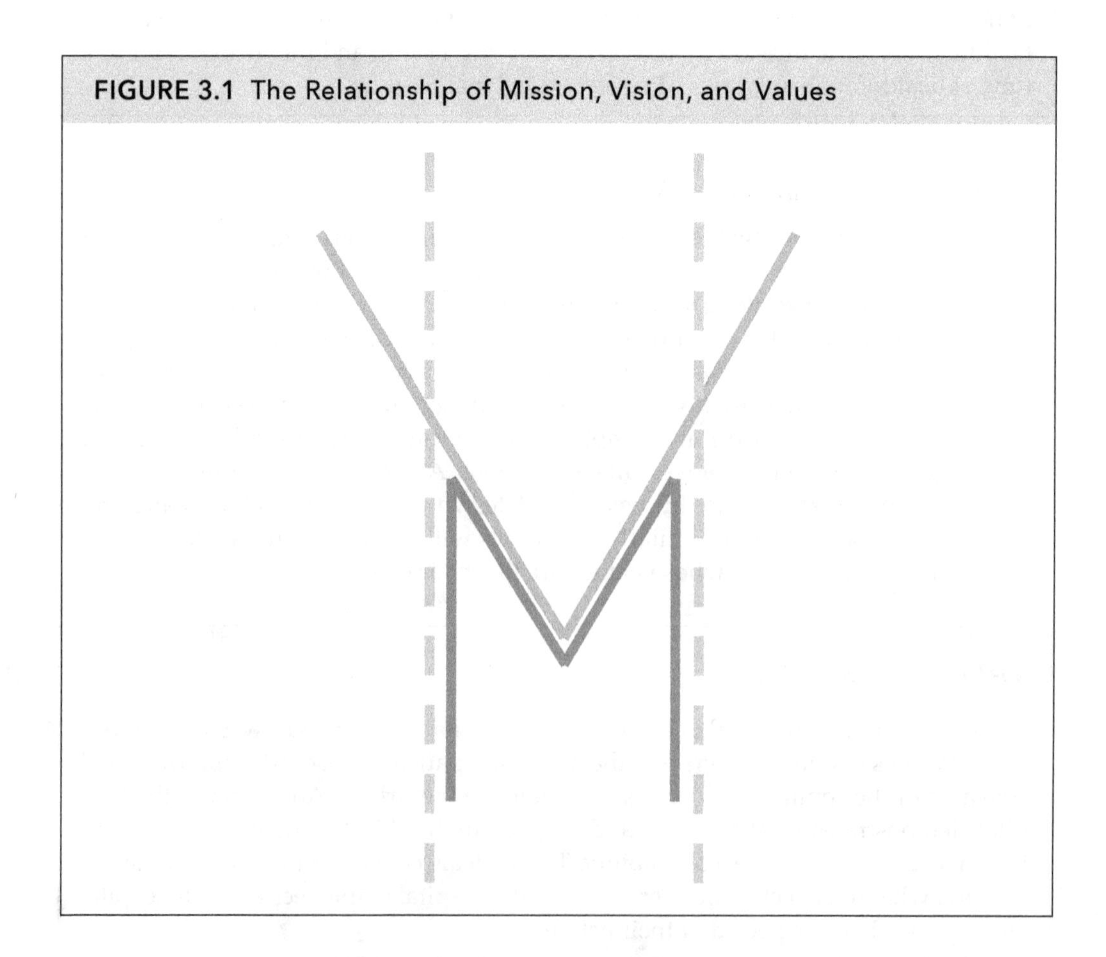

different from its original mission. This shift is a result of activities that are not planned or deliberate.

Causes of mission creep include:

- Personnel changes, particularly at the senior leadership or ownership level
- Financial opportunities, such as grant funding and contracts
- Reactions to changes in the external environment

As seen in the opening vignette, Tom's nonprofit organization was threatened by well-intentioned activities that resulted in mission creep. The way that organizations maintain the balance between working within the mission of the organization and the need to alter the mission to meet changing needs is to conduct a periodic review of the mission statement relative to operations. This review is typically completed during the annual review of the strategic plan.

CASE STUDY MEMORIAL HOSPITAL, INC.

The strategic planning committee's first task was to review the hospital's current mission, vision, and values statements.

MISSION

The mission of Memorial Hospital, Inc. is to provide compassionate, accessible, high-quality, cost-effective healthcare to the community, and to promote health.

VISION

To be remembered by each patient as providing the care and compassion we want for our families and ourselves.

VALUES

Integrity—adhering to a code of trust, fairness, and honesty
Compassion—caring for people in need and benevolence for people in general
Excellence—pursuing the highest level of service and quality in all that we do
Dignity—respecting one's worth as a human being
Teamwork—achieving common goals together
Responsibility—acting in honest, forthright, and fiscally responsible ways

The committee conducts a survey of employees, providers, community partners, payers, and other stakeholders to assess these statements. After analysis, the committee determines that the statements are reflective of the organization's purpose, where it wants to be in the future, and its philosophies. The committee recommends to the CEO that the statements be left intact, and the CEO agrees. The board ratified this decision at the last board meeting.

The following mission and vision statements worksheet provides direction for how you would write mission and vision statements in an organization.

MISSION AND VISION STATEMENTS WORKSHEET

THE MISSION STATEMENT

1. Write a statement for the following areas:
   - Internal operations statement:

     ____

     ____

     ____

     ____

   - External clientele statement:

     ____

     ____

     ____

     ____

   - Needs served statement:

     ____

     ____

     ____

     ____

2. Evaluate the statement.
   - Does it define boundaries within which your HCO will operate?

     ____

     ____

     ____

     ____

   - Does it define the need(s) that your HCO is attempting to meet?

     ____

     ____

     ____

     ____

- Does it reflect what kind of organization you need to be in order to achieve success in the future?

- Do you intend to have local, regional, national, or international scope?

- Does it define the market (patients/customers/clientele) that your HCO is reaching?

- Has there been input from appropriate organizational members?

- Does it include the word "service" or a word with a similar meaning?

3. Submit the mission statement to others familiar with your organization to evaluate your statement of purpose and offer suggestions on improving the statement. In other words, does the statement say to others what you want it to say?

VISION STATEMENT

1. Write statements that answer the following questions:
   - What do we want our organization to be like in the future?
   - What do we want to be known for in the future?
   - In what areas of our operation do we aspire to be the very best?
   - What do we want our employees to do in achieving the aforementioned aims?
2. Evaluate the vision statement.
   - Are the statements clearly phrased and understandable to all the HCO's employees?

- Are the statements actively phrased in order to generate energy and enthusiasm within the organization?

- Are the statements concise and memorable?

3. Submit the vision statement to others familiar with your organization to evaluate your statement and offer suggestions on improving the statement.

GLOSSARY OF TERMS

For-profit organization—an organization that is owned by investors or shareholders with an overarching purpose of maximizing shareholder wealth

Mission—an organization's purpose or reason for being

Mission creep—shift in focus to an organizational purpose that is different than the original mission

Mission statement—means for reporting the mission of an organization

Nonprofit organization (aka, **charitable organization**)—an organization that is exempt from federal and property taxes, exempt from federal taxation of interest paid on bonds, that may write off bad debt as an expense, and may receive tax-deductible contributions. Nonprofit designations are awarded by the Internal Revenue Service (IRS)

Organizational values—organizational principles that provide guidelines for beliefs, attitudes, and behaviors

Vision statement—an organization's future desired state, or where it hopes to be in the future

REFERENCES

American Hospital Association. (2018). Fast facts on US hospitals. Retrieved from https://www.aha.org/system/files/2018-02/2018-aha-hospital-fast-facts.pdf

Cleveland Clinic Mission Statement, Cleveland Clinic, 2018.

Forbes Corporate Communications. (2017). Forbes releases seventh annual world's most valuable brands list. *Forbes.* Retrieved from https://www.forbes.com/sites/forbespr/2017/05/23/forbes-releases-seventh-annual-worlds-most-valuable-brands-list/#33f042365b55

Internal Revenue Service. (n.d.). New requirements for 501(c)(3) hospitals under the Affordable Care Act. Retrieved from https://www.irs.gov/charities-non-profits/charitable-organizations/new-requirements-for-501c3-hospitals-under-the-affordable-care-act

King, D. L., Case, C. J., & Premo, K. M. (2010). Current mission statement emphasis: Be ethical and go global. *Academy of Strategic Management Journal, 9*(2), 71–87.

Mayo Clinic Health System Mission statement, Mayo Foundation for Medical Education and Research.

Williams, L. S. (2008). The mission statement: A corporate reporting tool with a past, present, and future. *Journal of Business Communication, 45*(2), 94–119. doi:10.1177/0021943607313989

CHAPTER 4

SITUATIONAL ANALYSIS

What's the use of running if you are not on the right road?

—German proverb

LEARNING OBJECTIVES

1. Distinguish between internal and external analyses.
2. Develop a sample strengths, weaknesses, opportunities, and threats (SWOT) analysis.
3. Define distinctive competencies.
4. Understand how a political, economic, social, technological, environmental, legal (PESTEL) chart can be used to categorize information about the external environment.
5. Develop a force field analysis and a gap analysis.

Until the 1900s, the primary mode of personal transportation in the United States involved a horse. A New England company manufactured whips that were used by those who drove buggies and prided itself on being "the best buggy whip manufacturer in America." When Henry Ford's Model T was made in volume, the whip company maintained its focus on buggy whips with the goal of remaining the best in the industry. Meanwhile, one of its competitors began to diversify its products to include leather seats for the new automobiles. Unfortunately for the first company, the market for buggy whips got smaller and smaller, forcing the buggy whip manufacturer out of business. During the same time, the market for automobile leather grew, as did the profits of the innovating company.

This story underscores the importance of periodically conducting a situational analysis. We have already noted that change is a certainty, and the best way to prepare for change is to see it coming. As Winston Churchill, prime minister of the United Kingdom, once said, "To improve is to change; to be perfect is to change often." Companies need to know why and how to change, and an environmental analysis provides data to guide necessary changes.

■ ■ ■

EXTERNAL AND INTERNAL ANALYSES

A healthcare organization, even one that is extremely successful, will fail in time if it continues to operate as it has done in the past. The reason we can be confident in this statement is because the environment in which healthcare organizations operate is continuously changing. In addition to the external environment, changes occurring inside the organization can also significantly affect its ability to meet its mission. Consider a very common surgical procedure, total knee arthroplasty (aka, total knee replacement).

When total knee replacements were first performed in the late 1960s, a typical treatment plan included an overnight stay in the hospital the night before surgery, surgery the following day, and up to a week in the hospital postsurgery. Since 1965, because most patients having joint replacement surgeries are over the age of 65, the procedure is covered by Medicare. For patients with 4 to 5 days of inpatient hospitalization under Medicare cost-based (fee-for-service) reimbursement, both the hospital and orthopedic surgeon could see significant financial gain. But those treatment plans were challenged by the implementation of Medicare's Inpatient Prospective Payment System (IPPS), commonly referred to as the Diagnosis-Related Group (DRG) system.

DRGs, first implemented in 1983, are used to calculate hospital inpatient Medicare reimbursement based on the average amount of resources that are needed to take care of a patient with a particular admitting diagnosis, adjusted for differences in labor costs. From the DRG calculation, a hospital knew how much it would be reimbursed for the admission and the average length of stay (ALOS) for patients with that condition. For a Medicare inpatient to be profitable, hospitals needed a physician to discharge the patient within the ALOS and/or the DRG funding stream. Treatment plans, and associated ALOS, for total knee replacement patients dropped. The Centers for Medicare and Medicaid Services (CMS) has since implemented a bundled payment model and removed total knee arthroplasty from the CMS inpatient-only list—meaning that the procedure is now covered in a hospital outpatient setting.

ALOS for total knee replacement dropped from 4.06 days in 2002 to 2.97 days in 2013 (Molloy, Martin, Moschetti, & Jevsevar, 2017). Imagine what would happen if a Medicare patient underwent total knee replacement surgery at a hospital where the surgeon prescribed a 4- to 5-day inpatient treatment plan. Failure to recognize and react to the regulatory and technology changes related to total knee replacements—changes in the external environment—would have severe financial consequences for a hospital.

The same hospital recognizes and adjusts to the DRGs for total knee replacement; however, it fails to recognize that the orthopedic surgeons with admitting privileges are approaching retirement age—a change in the internal environment. Failing to act and recruit new physicians who can perform total knee replacements in the hospital will eventually result in a decreased number of those procedures being performed in the hospital, and decreases in associated reimbursements.

SWOT ANALYSIS

The environment in which the healthcare organization operates—both internal and external—must be carefully monitored and evaluated as part of the planning process. One model for business review is the SWOT analysis. **SWOT** stands for **S**trengths, **W**eaknesses, **O**pportunities, and **T**hreats (see Figure 4.1), and in an ideal circumstance the organization is in balance with the environment over time.

Strengths and weaknesses are elements of the internal environment and indicate what the organization does well and where it struggles. **Strengths** are current characteristics of the organization that allow for outstanding performance. For example, a multispecialty practice has a staff of outstanding physicians; an ambulatory surgical center has state-of-the-art medical equipment; an oncology practice subscribes to scientifically and evidence-based practice; and a long-term care facility has high-end living facilities.

Weaknesses are organizational characteristics that increase costs, decrease quality, or have some other negative impact on operations. For example, a health insurance company does not have adequate endocrinologist coverage in the market; a primary care practice has two nursing vacancies and is unable to fill them; and a pharmacy lacks processes to prevent duplication of effort. Weaknesses should be analyzed to determine root causes (the underlying reason for the weakness), and to ensure that one weakness is not driving another. It is important to honestly assess strengths and weaknesses because an organization has the potential to control and change these internal factors.

Opportunities and threats are elements of the external environment, and an organization may have little or no control over their impact. **Opportunities** include new business initiatives that are available to an organization. Examples include an increase in the number of childbearing age women in a market where an OB/GYN practice is located; an opportunity to collaborate with different healthcare partners; and the introduction by the American Academy

FIGURE 4.1 SWOT Analysis Chart

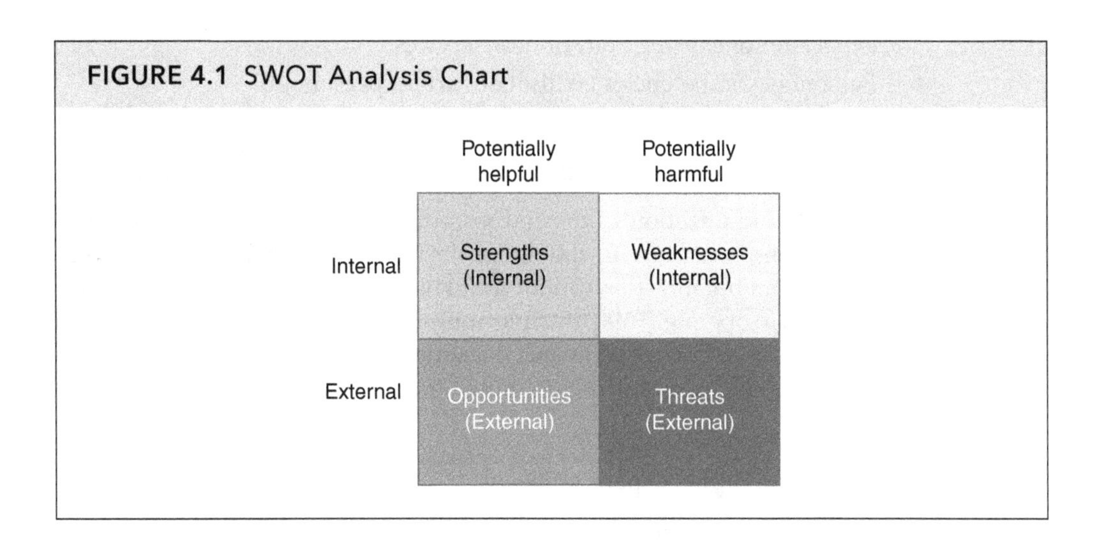

of Pediatrics of new clinical protocols that could be adopted by a pediatric practice. **Threats** are environmental forces that have the potential to harm the organization; for example, political or economic instability, decreases to a state Medicaid fee schedule, and an increase in the uninsured population in a market. It is important for an organization to keep its finger on the pulse of the environment because missed opportunities and unforeseen changes can have devastating consequences.

Internal Assessment

The first step of the SWOT analysis process is to gather and assess key internal data. The **internal assessment** (aka, **strategic audit)** focuses on an objective assessment of present operations to identify what the organization does well and where it needs to improve. Utilization of major services and programs, financial performance, and key indicators for the areas of facilities, equipment, and staff are typical components of the internal assessment. Strengths increase the likelihood of an organization to reach its goals, and weaknesses decrease that likelihood. The overarching goal is to maximize strengths and mitigate weaknesses.

Identifying strengths and weakness can be done systematically by analyzing the major sectors of the organization's operations. First, the organization's management structure/system should be evaluated to recognize:

- Characteristics of the organizational culture (e.g., patient/customer-driven versus financial performance-driven social values)
- Attributes of the management team (e.g., skills, experience, ages, values)
- Program performance (e.g., support, effectiveness, evaluation)
- Effectiveness of human resource management (e.g., open positions, pending retirements, supply and demand of licensed professionals)

Second, operational resources should be assessed, including:

- Capacity (e.g., number of licensed/staffed beds, potential for future expansion of existing and/or new services)
- Personnel competencies (skillset of current personnel)
- Cost structure (cost-efficiency, profitability)
- Technological capability (status of current equipment, ability to acquire)

Third, the organization's financial resources should be considered. There is a saying that is popular in the nonprofit world: "no money, no mission," meaning that an organization cannot fulfill its purpose unless it has the financial resources to operate. This principle applies to both nonprofit and for-profit organizations since both need financial resources to survive. Financial requirements to assess include but are not limited to:

- Short-term operating needs
- Long-term capital expansion needs
- Ability to access capital markets
- Expenses

- Donations
- Revenue cycle
- Cash flow
- Breakeven on new projects
- Debt-to-equity ratios
- Investments

Fourth, marketing capacity should be identified. The ability of an organization to get appropriate messaging to its target audience, driving utilization of services and associated revenue, is both a science and an art. This is one area where a "make or buy" decision is made—make the capacity in-house by hiring qualified marketing staff or buy the expertise via outside consultants.

Determining whether an activity should be considered a strength or a weakness can be accomplished using several benchmarking methods:

1. The activity can be assessed to determine how well it meets its operational goals. The outcomes of the activity can be compared to the activity's performance over time (trend analysis) and/or to other operational activities within the organization.
2. The activity can be compared to activities of peer organizations within the industry.
3. How well the activity is meeting expectations of funding sponsors is an important indicator of success and can be used to determine strength or weakness.
4. Using patient/customer feedback to determine whether the activity meets their needs.

Things that the organization does particularly well are known as **distinctive competencies**—superstrengths—that can be leveraged to gain a competitive edge in the marketplace. Identifying distinctive competencies and positioning the organization to use them to advantage is a critical part of the internal assessment process.

It is difficult but imperative that assessments of strengths and weaknesses are completed objectively so that a true picture of the organizational position emerges. While it is fairly easy to identify strengths, getting team members to recognize weaknesses and limitations can be challenging. Organizational politics may dictate that someone outside of the organization, such as a consultant, is necessary to gain a candid evaluation. The importance of an objective assessment cannot be overstated, as the identified strengths and weaknesses drive the ability of the organization to set realistic objectives.

Strengths and weaknesses by organizational sector can be presented using a table, as in Table 4.1. This presentation allows strategy implications for each strength and weakness to be reviewed quickly.

External Assessment

The **external environmental analysis** should evaluate the environmental conditions in which the organization currently operates and those in which it will

TABLE 4.1 Example of Strengths and Weaknesses by Organizational Sector

Management Structure/System	Strategy Implications
1. Strengths • Skilled management team 2. Weaknesses • Pharmacist shortage	1. Capacity to manage changing environment 2. Impact on service lines
Operational Resources	**Strategy Implications**
1. Strengths • Existing licensed beds 2. Weaknesses • Cost-effective operations	1. Expansion opportunity 2. Competitive advantage in securing bundled contracts
Financial Resources	**Strategy Implications**
1. Strengths • Good cash position 2. Weaknesses • High debt/equity ratio	1. Consider new or expanded service offerings 2. Must fund capital expansion through internal sources
Marketing Capacity	**Strategy Implications**
1. Strengths • Excellent public perception 2. Weaknesses • No in-house designer	1. New service could gain halo benefit in community 2. Outside consultant required for marketing design

likely operate in the future. This process serves to identify opportunities from which the organization might benefit, and threats that the organization should seek to mitigate or minimize. Environmental factors for analysis include, but are not limited to:

1. *Economic trends*, such as employment rates, poverty rates, increase/decrease in household income, inflation, and cost of capital
2. *Demographic trends*, such as aging population, number of women of childbearing age, urban/rural growth, and educational level
3. *Changes in services offered*, including public versus private providers, local versus national ownership, and how well the needs of the community are being met
4. *Trends in competition* from other healthcare providers that will affect patient and funding markets
5. *Trends in supply of healthcare professsionals*, such as shortages, the likelihood of sign-on bonuses, and changes in training requirements
6. *Changes in patient/client needs and social values*, including what members of the community feel is important and how well the organization is meeting those needs

7. *Reimbursement and regulatory factors*, such as entry/exit of payers in the market, changes to Medicaid fee schedules, and implementation of new regulations by the CMS

Opportunities and threats related to the environment are analyzed to determine if any action (strategy) should be developed to deal with them.

Data Sources

There are a variety of public healthcare information databases that can be accessed to provide demographic and other inputs into the external assessment. Examples include:

- Agency for Healthcare Research and Quality (AHRQ)
  - The AHRQ (www.ahrq.gov) is the health services research arm of the U.S. Department of Health and Human Services. The website provides links to research data, reports, tools, and funding mechanisms.
- Centers for Medicare and Medicaid Services (CMS)
  - The CMS (www.cms.gov) is a federal agency whose primary responsibility is to provide health insurance for qualified U.S. citizens aged 65 and older. The CMS also oversees the federal side of the Medicaid program. The CMS maintains extensive data on annual Medicare and Medicaid expenditures, the Children's Health Insurance Program (CHIP), and national health expenditures.
- County Health Rankings & Roadmaps
  - County Health Rankings & Roadmaps (www.countyhealthrankings.org) is a collaboration between the Robert Wood Johnson Foundation and the University of Wisconsin Population Health Institute. The rankings measure vital health factors on a county level.
- FedStats
  - FedStats (https://nces.ed.gov/partners/fedstat.asp) is a source for statistical information produced by more than 100 agencies of the federal government.
- GuideStar
  - GuideStar (www.guidestar.org) maintains data on nonprofit organizations, including mission, programs, and finances.
- Hospital Compare
  - Hospital Compare (www.healthdata.gov/dataset/hospital-compare) is a source of data through the Department of Health and Human Services, with a goal of increasing data accessibility to improve health outcomes.
- National Center for Health Statistics (NCHS)
  - The NCHS (www.cdc.gov/nchs) is the principal U.S. statistics agency and compiles statistical information collected primarily

through survey instruments for the purpose of guiding health policy and improving population health.

- NationMaster
  - NationMaster (www.nationmaster.com/index.php) is a massive central data source to geographically compare different nations.
- Nursing Home Compare
  - Nursing Home Compare (www.medicare.gov/NHCompare/home.asp) is a tool managed by the CMS to evaluate nursing homes at local, state, and national levels.
- StateMaster
  - StateMaster (www.statemaster.com/index.php) provides data on different states and allows comparisons across states.
- U.S. Census Bureau
  - The U.S. Census Bureau (www.census.gov) provides information from the American Community Survey (ACS), which collects population and housing data on an annual basis. The Census Bureau also collects population census data every 10 years, economic census data, and other data types through surveys.

PESTEL Chart

Some healthcare organizations find it beneficial to organize information about the external environment into categories presented in a **PESTEL Chart**, which can be used to complement a SWOT analysis. PESTEL is an acronym for factors that impact organizations:

- **P**olitical—governmental policies, governmental resource allocations, armed conflict, lobbying/campaigning activities by interest groups, changes in power/influence, and expectations for future changes
- **E**conomic—the economy (local, national, regional, global), economic status of communities/populations, infrastructure, expected direction of economic changes
- **S**ocial—cultural trends, demographics, population analytics, and social determinants of health
- **T**echnological—how a population uses technology, new innovation and technology, potential for innovation and change
- **E**nvironmental—global/national/regional/local environmental issues (e.g., air quality, climate change, water availability), environmental regulations, impact of weather, geographical location of services/patients
- **L**egal—current legislation, ethical issues, pending/future legislation, standards/oversight

Representatives from major stakeholder groups consider conditions in one of the areas, reviewing relevant data compiled by the strategic planning team. During a brainstorming session, the group identifies activities in the area considered that are either currently impacting the organization or will potentially impact the organization in the future. The activities are not addressed, nor are solutions developed, at this point; however, each is determined to be within the control of the organization or not. After each area is considered, a PESTEL Chart can be completed. An example PESTEL Chart for a local public health department is presented in Table 4.2.

Because factors within each of the six areas can vary across geographical markets (i.e., from county to county), a separate PESTEL Chart should be constructed for each operational area considered under the strategic plan.

The Role of Assumptions

When conducting an external analysis, major assumptions should be made concerning factors in which the organization has little or no control. By not

TABLE 4.2 PESTEL Chart for a Local Public Health Department

Political	Economic	Social	Technological
Local/state /regional regulations	State budget shortfalls	Percentage of uninsured population	Public health data collection systems
Federal regulations	Reductions in federal grants	Faith-based activities	Capacity for public health data analytics
Relationships with local elected officials	Internal financial security	Access to medical home	Ability to share data with stakeholders
	Public and private insurance billing capacity	Growth in Hispanic population	Access to real-time data
		High school graduation rates	

Legal	Environmental
Data-sharing agreements	Community health needs assessments
Disease-monitoring requirements	Implementation of health in all policies
ACA changes	New construction

Within control of Health Department

Within influence of Health Department

Outside control of Health Department

ACA, Affordable Care Act; ACS, American Community Survey.

making assumptions, the organization is assuming that the environment will remain the same—an assumption that we have noted is not likely to hold.

A nongovernmental organization (NGO) operating in South Africa was exploring mechanisms for a local community to generate resources toward self-sufficiency. The NGO noted the rich, fertile soil and deduced that there was an opportunity to partner with a tomato plant grower in Italy who had exceptional success growing large tomatoes. The NGO imported the plants to South Africa, hired local workers to farm the crops, and was rewarded with an abundant crop of tomatoes four to five times the normal size. As the tomatoes were near ripening, NGO officials reported the success of the project to their board. A few days after the board report, a herd of hippopotamuses invaded the gardens and consumed all of the produce, destroying agricultural equipment and supplies. One local farmer confided to the NGO administrator, "That's why we don't plant tomatoes."

Assumptions document the external situational trends that are projected to significantly impact operations. Examples of major assumptions include:

- Growth and aging in population will lead to increased demand for health services.
- Competition in the market will intensify.
- Pharmaceutical and technological advances will drive services to lower intensity delivery settings.
- The likelihood that physicians will offer ancillary services through offices will increase.
- As employers shift a greater percentage of the cost of providing health insurance benefits to employees, price sensitivity will increase.
- Labor shortages in nurses and pharmacists will occur.
- Significant governmental involvement in financing and regulation will occur.

Force Field Analysis

Increasing strengths, decreasing weaknesses, taking advantage of opportunities, and mitigating/minimizing threats require an organization to understand the forces driving these internal and external factors. A **force field analysis** (Lewin, 1951) is a method of examining the forces driving or hindering change, which recognizes that success is dependent on the number of forces driving change (positive) outweighing the number of forces hindering change (negative).

The first step is to brainstorm potential positive and negative forces, including an assessment of the strength of those forces, and capture those in a force field diagram (see Figure 4.2). The length of the arrow represents the strength of the force, which allows for a discussion of how to increase the forces that are positive for the desired change and to decrease the forces that are negative for the desired change.

The force field analysis is a useful tool for teams. Once the team can identify and understand forces that compel the organization, it is able to develop strategies to encourage or enhance those forces. Similarly, once the team can identify and understand forces that are holding back the organization, it can develop strategies to eliminate or mitigate these forces.

FIGURE 4.2 Force Field Diagram

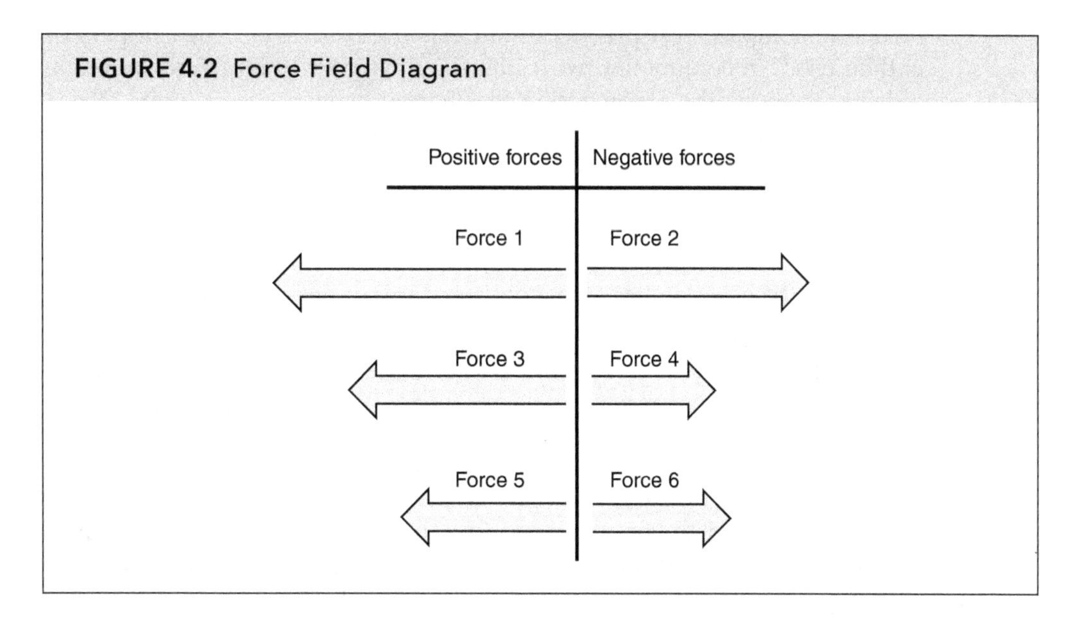

FORCE FIELD ANALYSIS EXAMPLE: MARKET EXPANSION

General Hospital's (fictitious name) strategic plan includes expanding services into Green County (fictitious) in a move to increase market share in the region. The hospital enjoys strong brand awareness and has a dominant position in its current market of five counties. The strategic plan implementation team completes the following Force Field Analysis for expanding a new Obstetrics and Gynecology (OB/GYN) practice in Green County:

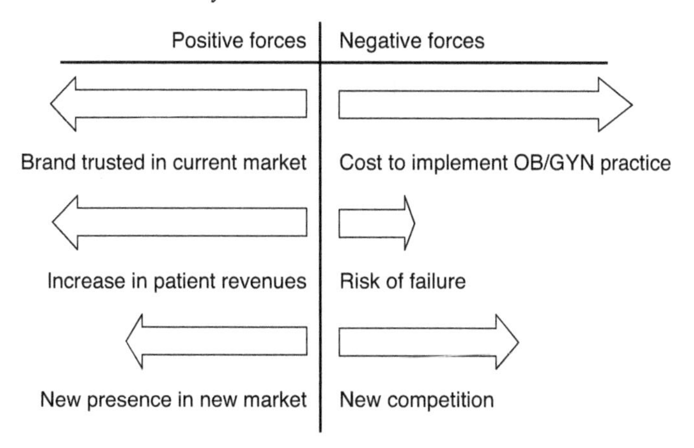

The staff believed that positive forces of brand image, potential for increased patient revenue, and having a new presence in a desirable market outweighed the forces of cost, risk of failure, and new competition. In light of the strategic planning SWOT analysis and the force field analysis, staff recommended establishing a new OB/GYN practice in Green County.

Gap Analysis

Another tool that is useful for teams is a **gap analysis**, which provides a format to compare best practices with existing processes. This comparison is then used, in conjunction with identified barriers to implementation, as a driver to move the organization to where it needs to be in terms of performance. Gap analysis can help an organization by informing the needs assessment process and helping to focus its goals. The steps in conducting gap analysis are:

1. Identify what is currently happening in the organization.
2. Define the best practice (aka, gold standard) or desired practice for the process/project.
3. Clarify the gap or discrepancy between current reality and desired state.
4. Determine objectives for the organization based on the identified gaps.

Implementing a gap analysis requires gathering data related to the process/project to be studied. Examples of data to consider include: outcomes from literature review, customer data (e.g., hospital admissions), governmental policies, and clinical care guidelines. A simple table can be constructed for each process/project to assist in decision making (Table 4.3).

TABLE 4.3 Gap Analysis Table

Current Practice	Desired Practice	Resources Required	Barriers	Strategies

A gap analysis for General Hospital's OB/GYN potential expansion into Green County might include the following:

Current Practice	Desired Practice	Resources Required	Barriers	Strategies
2% OB/GYN market share from Green County	8% OB/GYN market share from Green County	Clinic facility Providers and staff Equipment	Cost Competition	Lease facility 3-day per week presence

Once a gap analysis is completed, strategic options or alternatives should be developed and assumptions should be tested. **Scenario analysis** is a method in which multiple potential future states (or outcomes) are forecast. It is not constrained by events of the past, which may not capture the impact of changes in the environment; rather it uses both trends (the known) and uncertainties (the unknown) to predict a range of possible future scenarios. Each alternative future scenario includes a pathway that is required to reach that future state, which allows managers to explore the impact of change and to prepare for the future. Scenarios are generally formulated in terms of "best case," "worst case," and "most likely case" outcomes to account for the probability of future states occurring. The value of scenario analysis is that it encourages managers to see beyond biases that drive assumptions that may or may not hold true in the future.

While scenario analysis examines different situations in which a plan may be implemented, **sensitivity analysis** (aka, **"What-If" analysis**) considers how performance is affected by changes in an assumption of the strategic plan. Sensitivity analysis occurs within a defined scenario and can be used to determine the optimum input for a given outcome. Managers will often apply sensitivity analysis to the best case identified in scenario analysis.

A hospital, in its review of disaster plans, will consider several planning scenarios. For example, if there is a likelihood that a tornado could impact the service area, the hospital will need to estimate the number of casualties—both morbidity and mortality—related to the disaster. This information can be estimated through consultation with local health department and emergency management offices. Once the number of casualties is estimated, the hospital identifies all resources that would be required to treat the casualties and maintain operations. Resources include, for example, staffed hospital beds, operating rooms, ventilators, generators, food/water/medical supplies, transportation, and personnel.

It is also important to identify external resources and operational capacity to assist. For example, in a disaster a tertiary care hospital would work with regional community hospitals to coordinate transfer of less-critical patients, including those already in the hospital, to those facilities to free up capacity in the tertiary care hospital to receive critical patients. Once the required resources are identified, the hospital can then identify the gaps in the resources required and the resources currently available. This gap will need to be closed in order for the hospital to effectively manage the disaster.

Hospitals develop **contingency plans** for non-normal events such as disasters that affect hospital operations. The need for a contingency plan, often referred to as "Plan B," emerges from risk analyses of critical business functions, determination of level of risk, and prioritization of potential risk scenarios. A contingency plan will identify a specific trigger (e.g., disaster event) that causes normal operations to be interrupted and the contingency plan activated. Actions to be taken by time period, resource requirements, and impact on operational areas are addressed in the plan, so that the plan can be implemented immediately when needed. While contingency plans are written to respond to crises, their primary goal is to return the organization to normal operations as quickly as possible.

Analysis Paralysis

The environmental assessment is a critical component of the strategic planning process, and all efforts should be made to analyze data that will inform necessary decisions for the organization. However, there are near unlimited data points and variables that could be considered in such analysis. It is imperative that organizations avoid **analysis paralysis**—a situation where analysis does not have an end point and decisions are never made. So, how do you avoid analysis paralysis and still consider the relevant internal and external factors? The key is to prioritize the data investigated and the decisions made, keeping in mind the larger purpose for conducting the analysis. Recognize that there is a cost–benefit relationship in this process, with costs (e.g., personnel, money, time) being traded for benefit (e.g., well-informed decisions). Perfection is something few, if any, organizations can (or should) afford.

CASE STUDY MEMORIAL HOSPITAL, INC.

Memorial Hospital conducts an annual review of its strategic planning activities and renews its strategic plan every 3 years. While the Department of Planning and Marketing is primarily responsible for developing the strategic plan, employees and stakeholders are heavily involved in the process.

The internal assessment consists of surveys and focus groups of key stakeholders (including employees), service utilization trend data, and financial statement analysis, to name a few. Data collected and analyzed for the external assessment include data from publicly available databases to determine economic trends, demographic trends, changes in services offered, trends in competition, supply/demand of healthcare professionals, patient/client needs and social values, and reimbursement and regulatory factors.

Significant areas identified through the internal and external analysis were vetted through a process that included review by management, the board of directors, and other stakeholders. The purpose of this process was to categorize areas according to the magnitude of potential impact on the organization.

Sample outcomes from the external evaluation include the following:

GOVERNMENT

Opportunities

1. Strong relationship exists with city councils and health departments. Recent natural disaster and hospital partnerships enhanced these relationships. Opportunity for collaboration on grants and support in the community is present for hospital projects.

Threats

1. Decreased governmental reimbursement (Medicare and Medicaid).

(continued)

CASE STUDY MEMORIAL HOSPITAL, INC. (*continued*)

ECONOMY

Opportunities

1. Numbers of privately insured citizens are increasing with opportunity for increased revenues.

Threats

1. Potential closure of paper mill in secondary market would lead to an increase in uninsured patients from that region.

TECHNOLOGY

Opportunities

1. Infrastructure in rural communities allows for tele-health opportunities.

Threats

1. Ambulatory Surgery Center has plans to acquire the latest robotic surgery equipment.

SOCIAL TRENDS

Opportunities

1. Population is increasing as well as increased household income in much of service area with opportunity to increase service revenues.

Threats

1. There is the potential closure of paper mill in secondary market.

PATIENTS/CLIENTS

Opportunities

1. The increased population of women of childbearing age affords opportunity for women's and children's services revenue.

Threats

1. Potential closure of paper mill in secondary market would lead to an increase in uninsured patients from that region.

REIMBURSEMENT SOURCES/SPONSORSHIP

Opportunities

1. New private insurance company offering health insurance plans in market affords opportunity to increase privately insured patients and revenues.

Threats

1. Decreased governmental reimbursements for Medicare- and Medicaid-covered services are possible.

(*continued*)

CASE STUDY MEMORIAL HOSPITAL, INC. (*continued*)

COMPETING HEALTHCARE ORGANIZATIONS

Opportunities

1. Partnership opportunities could exist for contract work through VA hospital.

Threats

1. A private hospital may target services to childbearing women in affluent communities.

Sample outcomes from the internal evaluation include the following:

Strengths

1. Knowledge, skills, and experience of current CEO (hired 4 years ago) from career with large integrated delivery system
2. Dominant market share in primary and secondary service areas
3. Full range of inpatient and outpatient services
4. Brand recognition as healthcare provider of choice in markets

Weaknesses

1. Stressed relationship with many members of the medical staff
2. High ALOS and average patient expenses
3. Excessive test ordering by some members of the medical staff
4. Lack of ownership of a health insurance plan

Sample assumptions include the following:

1. Involvement by federal government in healthcare delivery will continue to increase. Modifications of Medicare and Medicaid payments will be made within the next 5 years.
2. Philanthropic donations will decrease due to changes in tax laws.
3. Employers will take an increasingly aggressive position in trying to control the cost of healthcare coverage for their employees.
4. Technological advances will increase at a rapid pace, and more inpatient services will be pushed to the outpatient market.
5. Risk will shift from insurers to providers through population health initiatives.
6. Quality of services will lead to expansion of services.
7. The cost of long-term care services will be further scrutinized as demand for services continues to increase.

The following situational analysis and assumptions worksheet will aid you in completing a SWOT analysis.

SITUATIONAL ANALYSIS AND ASSUMPTIONS WORKSHEET

Step 1. Internal Operations Analysis: Using the following question guides and your own information, list key strengths and weaknesses for each of the following sectors of your healthcare organization's operations.

Management and Planning Systems

Use these questions to help you prepare a list of strengths and weaknesses for this portion of the healthcare organization's operations.

Do you have a planning system?

____

____

____

____

How does it work?

____

____

____

____

Is the organizational structure of your healthcare organization allowing effective use of resources?

____

____

____

____

Is control centralized or decentralized?

____

____

____

____

Are performance measures and information system controls in evidence? What are they?

What staffing needs do you have?

Is there a motivation problem?

Is your current strategy defined? Is it working?

How efficient are operations?

What is your synopsis of the current management situation?

Now list your strengths and weaknesses for this section of your healthcare organization's operations.

Strengths

Weaknesses

Financial Resources

Use these questions to help you prepare your strengths and weaknesses list for this portion of your healthcare organization's operation.

What is your current financial situation?

Do you have regular financial statements prepared?

What tools would be beneficial in analysis?

Do you have pro forma statements for revenue centers such as rehabilitative care, hospice care, and so on?

Do you have a cash budget?

Do you have a capital budget?

Has a ratio analysis been prepared?

Do you understand the time value of money?

Do you understand and use break-even analysis?

Have you analyzed current financial policies?

Do you have cash policies?

How are accounts receivable analyzed?

How are accounts payable analyzed?

Do you control inventory levels?

Do you have a debt retirement plan?

Give a synopsis of your current financial situation.

Accounting Analysis:

Depreciation procedures?

Tax considerations?

Decentralized/centralized operations?

Responsibility accounting?

Tools beneficial in analysis:

Do you have budgets (short- and long-range) established?

Do you perform variance analysis comparing actual against planned performance?

What costing methods are used?

Do you do contribution margin analysis?

Are there adequate controls, especially of cash, for each of your healthcare organization's programs?

What is your synopsis of the current accounting situation?

Now list your strengths and weaknesses for this section of your healthcare organization's operations.

Strengths

Weaknesses

Marketing Resources

Use these questions to help you prepare your strengths and weaknesses list for this portion of your healthcare organization's operation.

Have you established marketing policies?

Have you established what you will and will not do in marketing your services?

Have you identified your patients/clients?

Have you identified your funding/reimbursement sponsors?

What are your competitors' services and products, level of demand, and relative market positions?

What are your distribution systems and location of facilities and how effective are they?

Is your services' price/fee structure current and appropriate?

What promotional (advertising, sales promotion, and personal selling) activities are you using?

What is your synopsis of the current marketing situation?

Now list your strengths and weaknesses for this section of your healthcare organization's operations.

Strengths

____

____

____

____

Weaknesses

____

____

____

____

Operations or Services Resources

Use these questions to help you prepare a list of strengths and weaknesses for this section of the organization's operations.

What are your operations' capacities?

____

____

____

____

In what shape are your facilities?

____

____

____

____

What is the age and serviceability of your equipment?

____

____

____

____

How automated are your operations?

What are your transportation capabilities?

Are safety programs adequate?

How effective is your inventory control?

Do you use quality control systems?

Now list your strengths and weaknesses for this section of your healthcare organization's operations.

Strengths

Weaknesses

____

____

____

____

Next, evaluate the services of your professional staff:

Range of services offered?

____

____

____

____

Number of services rendered and patients served by service category?

____

____

____

____

Number and estimated years to retirement of professional staff by services category?

____

____

____

____

Have you listed and analyzed all major internal factors with significant impact on your organization's operations?

____

____

____

____

Step 2. External Environmental Analysis: From industry surveys and your own sources of information, take the organization's pulse. You are looking for trends—what is going on now and how this relates to past trends that have influenced your healthcare organization's performance. From this analysis, list key opportunities and threats for each of the following environmental sectors.

Government

Opportunities

1. ______________________
2. ______________________
3. ______________________

Threats

1. ______________________
2. ______________________
3. ______________________

Economy

Opportunities

1. ______________________
2. ______________________
3. ______________________

Threats

1. ______________________
2. ______________________
3. ______________________

Technology

Opportunities

1. ______________________
2. ______________________
3. ______________________

Threats

1. ______________________
2. ______________________
3. ______________________

Social Trends

Opportunities

1. ______________________

2. ______________________________
3. ______________________________

Threats

1. ______________________________
2. ______________________________
3. ______________________________

Patients/Clients

Opportunities

1. ______________________________
2. ______________________________
3. ______________________________

Threats

1. ______________________________
2. ______________________________
3. ______________________________

Reimbursement Sources/Sponsorship

Opportunities

1. ______________________________
2. ______________________________
3. ______________________________

Threats

1. ______________________________
2. ______________________________
3. ______________________________

Competing Healthcare Organizations

Opportunities

1. ______________________________
2. ______________________________
3. ______________________________

Threats

1. ______________________________

2. ____

3. ____

Next, evaluate your external analysis:

Have you listed several international/national trends that affect your healthcare organization?

____

____

____

____

Have you listed several local trends that affect your healthcare organization?

____

____

____

____

Have you identified trends unique to your healthcare organization (e.g., availability of certain healthcare professionals)?

____

____

____

____

Have you listed several of your most important competitors?

____

____

____

____

Which are growing?

____

____

____

____

Which are declining?

____

___

___

___

What are the successful ones doing?

___

___

___

___

Step 3. Development of Assumptions: List the major assumptions on which your plan is based.

1. ___
2. ___
3. ___
4. ___
5. ___

GLOSSARY OF TERMS

Analysis paralysis—a situation where analysis does not have an end point and decisions are never made

Contingency plan—developed for non-normal events such as disasters

Distinctive competencies—in a SWOT analysis, superstrengths that can be leveraged to gain a competitive edge in the marketplace

External environmental analysis—an objective evaluation of the environmental conditions in which the organization currently operates and those in which it will likely operate in the future

Force field analysis—a method of examining the forces driving or hindering change, which recognizes that success is dependent on the number of forces driving change (positive) outweighing the number of forces hindering change (negative)

Gap analysis—an assessment that provides a format to compare best practices with existing practices, with the goal of improving performance

Internal assessment (aka, **strategic audit**)—an objective analysis of current operations to identify what the organization does well and where it needs to improve

Opportunities—in a SWOT analysis, new business initiatives that are available to an organization

PESTEL Chart—a method of organizing information about the external environment into categories: political, economic, social, technological, environmental, and legal

Scenario analysis—a method in which multiple potential future states (or outcomes) are forecast

Sensitivity analysis (aka, **"What-If" analysis)**—a method that considers how performance is affected by changes in assumptions made during the strategic planning process

Strengths—in a SWOT analysis, current characteristics of the organization that allow for outstanding performance

SWOT analysis—an assessment of the internal (strengths and weaknesses) and external (opportunities and threats) environment

Threats—in a SWOT analysis, environmental forces that have the potential to harm the organization

Weaknesses—in a SWOT analysis, organizational characteristics that increase costs, decrease quality, or have some other negative impact on operations

REFERENCES

Lewin, K. (1951). *Field theory in social science.* New York, NY: Harper and Row.

Molloy, I. B., Martin, B. I., Moschetti, W. E., & Jevsevar, D. S. (2017). Effects of the length of stay on the cost of total knee and total hip arthroplasty from 2002 to 2013. *Journal of Bone and Joint Surgery American Volume, 99*(5), 402–407. doi:10.2106/JBJS.16.00019

CHAPTER 5

OBJECTIVES

Strategy 101 is about choices: You can't be all things to all people.

—Michael E. Porter
Economist, researcher, and author

LEARNING OBJECTIVES

1. Describe the importance of setting objectives.
2. Differentiate between short-term and long-term objectives.
3. Discuss why organizations might be hesitant to set clear objectives.
4. Distinguish a well-written objective from a poorly written objective.
5. Write specific, measurable, achievable, relevant, and time-bound (SMART) objectives.

"What happened? Two months ago you were so excited about your promotion that you couldn't stop talking about it!" Jesse said to Ann. It was 2 months to the day when Ann had received her promotion, and the two were having lunch at their favorite spot. But Ann was less than enthusiastic. "Well, you know this project has been ongoing for over a year, and that I really thought I could make a difference in this new role. But now I know why they removed Frank as project manager. The budget is almost exhausted, the deadline has been moved up, and the project team is at a loss to think of how the project can be completed successfully. What am I going to do?!" Jesse looked over at Ann, "Have you looked at the root cause for an explanation of what is going wrong?" "Yes I did," said Ann "and I traced the problem back to the objectives. They were written without much detail! For example, the overarching objective is 'To release an update to the software in time for the annual conference.' But I need to rely on several other managers and their departmental staff in order to make this happen—and they are all tied up with other projects! It's as if someone wrote the objective without thought as to how it would be accomplished, the resources that would be required, and the necessary authority to get it done. And now I'm on the hook for it!" Ann wondered if the project could be salvaged in time, and her career.

ROLE OF OBJECTIVES

Once the mission of the healthcare organization has been defined and internal/external analysis has been completed, the organization is ready to write its relevant objectives. **Objectives** are clear, concise, measurable, written statements that convey what the organization wants to accomplish over a specific period of time. A responsible person or persons should be assigned for each objective, so that accountability is maintained.

General objectives must be met by all healthcare organizations. Patient safety influences each decision, action, or product. Cost reduction affects both for-profit and nonprofit organizations, as organizations that cannot operate efficiently suffer a strategic disadvantage. Another determining factor for success is patient satisfaction, which requires a balance of competence, compassion, and openness. Operating in one of the most heavily regulated industries in the economy, healthcare organizations and providers must pay particular attention to regulatory compliance. And improving the health of populations is an important consideration. Failure to address any of these foundational areas can lead to threats to organizational viability.

Short-term objectives are written for the operating period (typically, within 1 year), while **long-term objectives** typically span 3 to 5 years. It is common for healthcare organizations to focus on at least four areas of objectives:

1. Services offered
2. Staffing
3. Funding (service reimbursement, donations, and other funding)
4. Constituents served

Objectives should be established for all key result areas of the healthcare organization's operations. **Key result areas** are those that are most likely to impact performance. For example, key result areas for a clinic could be:

- Percentage of physicians who are board certified
- Number and quality of services offered
- Number of patients by service type
- Successful treatment rates
- Financial condition
- Status of facilities
- Patient satisfaction

An example of a productivity objective for patient care services is to reduce the number of home visits per patient by 10% (versus the last 12-month period) over the next 12 months. Reducing long-term debt to 25% of equity over the next 5 years is an example of a financial objective. And a patient/client services objective could be to develop and implement an elder care service within 18 months.

Objectives should be set across operational areas and subunits/departments within the organization. Recall that plans are written to move the organization forward in achieving its mission, or reason for being. Therefore, all plans at different levels across the organization should work in concert toward this overall goal—consistency with organizational objectives and purpose must be considered when writing objectives. All objectives, regardless of level within the organization, are informed by the analysis conducted in the environmental assessment. An example of how data are used in setting objectives may be helpful.

USING DATA IN SETTING OBJECTIVES

Helping Hands Nursing Home, Inc. desires to expand services and has been tracking hospice activities in its market. The nursing home has capacity for additional patients. Helping Hands reaches out to the five hospice programs in the community via survey, and learns that the hospice programs are hospitalizing patients for brief periods of medication adjustments. The nursing home sees an opportunity to provide similar service, as its existing staff of registered nurses, under the direction of the medical director, can manage this type of medication service. The advantage to the hospice programs is that the nursing home could provide the same service at a lower cost.

Helping Hands completes an analysis to determine how much facility resources would be required to implement this project:

Potential for Hospice Medication Program

1. Average number of hospice patients across five programs = 150
2. Average percentage of hospice patients hospitalized for medication management at any one time = 10%
3. Average number of hospice patients at any one time using inpatient hospital medication management = 15
4. Estimated percentage of hospice patients receiving medication management whose condition allows for administration in a nursing home setting = 90%
5. Total average number of hospice medication patients = 13.5 (15 × .90)
6. Initial estimate of acceptance of the program by referring physicians = 60%
7. Initial target market for program = 8.1 patients (13.5 × .60)

After analysis, Helping Hands is able to develop an objective that will allow expansion in this new operational area with a commitment of eight beds.

Clearly written objectives serve as a road map for the organization, answering the question Where do we want to go? The second fundamental purpose of objectives is to provide evaluation of organizational performance. Objectives are also strategically important in evaluating performance. One way to think about objectives is to consider which organizational programs you would choose to discuss if you were to meet with your board for 1 hour. You are likely to have time to discuss only two to four objectives per program area.

While it may seem evident why clear objectives are a required part of planning for success, there are several reasons why organizations are hesitant to set them:

1. Setting objectives allows for projects to continue even after they no longer serve the needs of the organization.
2. Some activities require time commitments that do not immediately meet the needs of the organization.
3. It is feared that strict evaluation of activities might undermine their mission to serve those in need.
4. Some managers fear accountability.

Executive leadership must drive the importance of strategic planning, including the necessity and benefits of setting good objectives.

Characteristics of Good Objectives–SMART

In order to monitor progress toward achieving desired outcomes, strong written objectives that accurately measure progress are required. A **SMART objective** is specific, measurable, achievable, relevant, and time-bound.

- *Specific*—Objectives should be well-defined and not ambiguous. There should not be any room for misunderstanding. Having written objectives goes a long way in ensuring specificity. Consider questions such as What exactly will we do? and Who is responsible for making sure this objective is completed?
- *Measurable*—Objectives should have precise definition and qualification in order to be assessed for progress toward completion. Measurable objectives are quantifiable and should show success or impact over time, or the lack thereof. Consider questions such as What percentage of change is acceptable and how long should it take? and How much change will occur?
- *Achievable*—Objectives should stretch the organization to produce, but should be achievable given available resources (e.g., time, money, skill). Objectives that cannot be achieved can produce low morale within the organization and among external stakeholders. Consider questions such as What will it take for this objective to be accomplished? and Can this objective be achieved given the time frame?
- *Relevant*—Objectives should align with the mission of the organization. As stated previously, consistency across the organization is essential. Consider questions such as If this objective is completed, will it move us toward completing our mission? and Is it worth the effort to measure this objective?
- *Time-bound*—Objectives should be written with a time frame, and should be achievable within that time frame. Consider questions such as When do we need for this objective to be completed? and Is the time frame outlined realistic?

EXAMPLES OF POORLY WRITTEN OBJECTIVES

- *Objective:* To lower the rate of medication errors in the ICU
  Criticism: How much is "lower?" How will we know if and when error rates reach the desired level? In addition, it does not include a time frame for completion.
  Improvement: To lower the rate of medication errors in the ICU by 10% within 12 months
- *Objective:* To increase occupancy rate
  Criticism: By how much? If the number of inpatients increases by one per day, this objective will be met. But is that really what is desired? In addition, it does not include a time frame for completion.
  Improvement: To increase the occupancy rate by 5% in the next 12 months
- *Objective:* To increase advertising expenditures by 15% over the next 12 months
  Criticism: Advertising is an activity that drives a result, not an end unto itself. What is the intention of adding the additional advertising?
  Improvement: To increase patient revenues by 10% per year over the next 3 years, with the help of increased advertising expenditures of 15% per year
- *Objective:* To be the best healthcare organization of our type in our market
  Criticism: What is the measure of "best?" Is it the number of patients served? Or level of reimbursement? Number of new programs started? Services offered?
  Improvement: To become the number one healthcare organization of its kind in the 13-county area in terms of number of patients served within the next 3 years

Objectives that meet these criteria are much more likely to serve their purpose, and will be more effective in driving the development of strategies (Chapter 6).

Practical suggestions for writing objectives include:

1. Start with an action verb, since achieving the objective will come as a result of a specific action.
2. Specify a major result to be accomplished for each objective. This will help you to know when the objective is achieved.
3. Set a target date for completion.
4. Ensure that the objective relates to the mission statement.
5. Make sure the objective is understandable by all stakeholders working to achieve the objective.
6. Write objectives that are possible to achieve.

Descriptive words for strategy statements include the following:

Provide	Develop	Deliver	Manage
Partner	Collaborate	Coordinate	Administer
Promote	Support	Contribute	Stimulate
Build	Expand	Extend	Streamline
Fund	Resource	Subsidize	Contract
Identify	Investigate	Survey	Research
Review	Consult	Evaluate	Report
Raise	Recognize	Celebrate	Document

Establishing well-conceived SMART objectives increases an organization's chance of successfully pursuing its mission, and encourages all stakeholders to be on the same page. Involving people in the organization early, and continuing to get their feedback as objectives are amended in iterations, will go a long way in terms of acceptance.

CASE STUDY MEMORIAL HOSPITAL, INC.

The mission of Memorial Hospital, Inc. is to provide compassionate, accessible, high-quality, cost-effective healthcare to the community, and to promote health.

After a review of the results from the environmental analysis, the committee decides to recommend objectives in four key areas.

1. **Economy**
   a. Increase in the number of privately insured citizens affords an opportunity to increase private pay revenues. Five counties have been identified with the greatest potential for increasing hospital revenue. The hospital realizes its greatest margin (revenues less expenses) from private health insurance payers.

      OBJECTIVE 1.1: To increase private insurance patient revenues in the five identified (based on growth of privately insured population) counties by 5% in the next 12 months, by targeting the five counties with advertising and physician relations campaigns. The chief operating officer (COO) is responsible for this objective.

   b. There is the potential closure of the paper mill in the secondary market. The paper mill provides private health insurance benefits to employees and their dependents, and is a source of revenue for the hospital.

      OBJECTIVE 1.2: To partner with management of the paper mill, in correlation with city and county officials, to explore options

(*continued*)

CASE STUDY MEMORIAL HOSPITAL, INC. (*continued*)

for closure. Pending a decision to close, work with city and county officials to identify job relocation strategies for paper mill employees. Activities will occur during all 3 years of the strategic plan. While this objective is not specifically measurable, the financial impact of the plant closure on the hospital would be significant. The CEO is responsible for this objective.

2. **Technology**
   a. New infrastructure in rural communities allows for tele-health opportunities.

      OBJECTIVE 2.1: To develop and implement tele-health in three new markets, focusing on delivering specialist consults, in the next 18 months. The chief medical officer (CMO) is responsible for this objective.

   b. An ambulatory surgery center (ASC), opened by a group of surgeons who have privileges at the hospital, has plans to acquire the latest robotic surgery equipment (da Vinci Surgical System). Adoption of this technology by the ASC would have an adverse impact on surgeries performed at Memorial Hospital, and associated revenues. While the hospital has some robotic capability, the hospital's Medical Technology Committee has completed a cost–benefit analysis for acquiring the da Vinci Surgical System and recommends implementation.

      OBJECTIVE 2.2: To acquire the da Vinci Surgical System and train providers in the next 12 months. The CMO is responsible for this objective.

3. **Competition**
   a. The local VA hospital does not currently offer some surgical services, creating an opportunity for Memorial Hospital to contract for those services.

      OBJECTIVE 3.1: To implement a contract in the next 12 months with the VA hospital to provide surgical services not currently offered at the VA. The Office of Legal Counsel is responsible for this objective.

   b. There continues to be a demographic trend of increased numbers of women of childbearing age in several affluent communities in the hospital's primary market. The private hospital is targeting those communities for their services.

      OBJECTIVE 3.2: To increase women's and children's services private insurance patient revenues in the identified (based on growth of childbearing age population) communities by 2% in the next 12 months, by targeting these communities with advertising campaigns. The COO is responsible for this objective.

(*continued*)

CASE STUDY MEMORIAL HOSPITAL, INC. (*continued*)

4. **Operations**

   a. Memorial Hospital's average length of stay (ALOS) and patient care expenses are significantly higher than peer institutions, and analyses indicate variance in length of stay and ordering profiles across admitting physicians.

      OBJECTIVE 4.1: To decrease ALOS to within the 40th percentile of peer institutions in the next 24 months. The medical operating officer (CMO) is responsible for this objective.

      OBJECTIVE 4.2: To conduct a review of the ordering profiles of all admitting physicians over the next 6 months using the Order Entry System to compare order histories by diagnosis with best practices for a specific illness.

The following objectives worksheet will aid you in developing objectives for your healthcare organization's operations.

OBJECTIVES WORKSHEET

Answer These Questions First

1. To what do your objectives need to relate: patients, services, revenues, and professional staffing? What about other key result areas?

   ____

   ____

   ____

   ____

2. What needs to happen for your program to be successful? In other words, how many people need to be served by the program?

   ____

   ____

   ____

   ____

3. When do you want this to happen? By what specific date?

   ____

   ____

Now Write Your Objectives

Use the information in your preceding answers to write statements of objectives for each key result area.

Objective 1:

Objective 2:

Objective 3:

Test Your Objectives

Now test each statement using the following criteria:

Is each statement relevant to the basic purpose of your organization?

1.

2.

3.

Is each statement practical?

1.

2.

3.

Does each statement provide a challenge?

1. ______________________________

2. ______________________________

3. ______________________________

Is each stated in objectively measurable terms?

1. ______________________________

2. ______________________________

3. ______________________________

Do you have a specific date for completion?

1. ______________________________

2. ______________________________

3. ______________________________

Does each statement contribute to a balance of activities in line with your healthcare organization's strengths and weaknesses?

1. ______________________________

2. ______________________________

3. ______________________________

GLOSSARY OF TERMS

Key result areas—operational areas that are most likely to impact performance

Long-term objectives—objectives that are written for a period of time outside of the current operating period, typically 3 to 5 years

Objectives—clear, concise, measurable, written statements that convey what the organization wants to accomplish over a specific period of time

Short-term objectives—objectives that are written for the operating period (typically, within 1 year)

SMART objective—an objective that is specific, measurable, achievable, relevant, and time-bound

CHAPTER 6

STRATEGIES AND OPERATIONAL PLANS

Strategy without tactics is the slowest route to victory. Tactics without strategy is the noise before defeat.

—Sun Tzu
Chinese general and military strategist

LEARNING OBJECTIVES

1. Define strategy and its relationship to objectives.
2. Describe common organizational constraints that limit strategy.
3. Determine why a specific differentiation strategy would be used by an organization.
4. Apply a growth-share matrix to evaluate an organization's products/services.
5. Classify operational strategies.
6. Explain how to enhance budgeting within an organization.

Wes could not wait. Yesterday he had graduated with his undergraduate degree, and in 3 hours he would be starting a dream backpacking trip across western Europe! As the image of the plane moved closer to the shores of France, Wes pulled out his tablet and reviewed his plans for the next 3 months. He had been thoughtful about traveling across as much of Europe as possible—it was his lifelong goal, after all. He had his backpack with clothing and essentials, his passport, and felt confident that he had enough money for the trip. He had left copies of his passport and his itinerary with family and friends at home, and notified the State Department of his travel plans using the Smart Traveler Enrollment Program (STEP). He could not wait to land at Charles de Gaulle airport and head to his first destination, La Loupe near the Parc Naturel Regional du Perche. His plan was to spend the next week using La Loupe as a sort of base camp, from which he could visit Le Perche, Chartres and its cathedral, Bellême, Châteaudun, and La Ferté-Bernard.

As Wes headed to the metro to catch a train to La Loupe, he studied the local map he was able to purchase at a kiosque. His goal of maximizing the amount of time he could use to explore each location left little room for error in his schedule; however, Wes became concerned that he likely overestimated the amount of time it would take to travel to and from La Loupe. Could he arrange lodging on the fly? Or would he cut his time or number of destinations? He would make the best of it, but the trip was not starting off as well as he had planned. Wes decided he would spend that night at a café reviewing his route and planned activities and make the necessary adjustments to his plans. It may take his first day at La Loupe, but Wes would work to develop better strategies to meet his objectives.

■■■

Once objectives for the planning period have been finalized, the next step in the strategic planning process is to formulate strategies to achieve each objective. **Strategy** may be defined as the course of action an organization takes to complete its objective. Developing strategies is both a science and an art; a product of logic and creativity. The science includes accumulating and allocating necessary resources, matching organizational strengths with opportunities in the environment, while working within resource constraints (e.g., time, money, personnel). The art of developing strategies is evident in how resources are utilized—for example, motivating personnel to ensure that the strategy is successfully implemented while being sensitive to environmental resources. Successful strategies should possess the following:

1. Focus on where the organization wants to be in the future
2. Match internal strengths and distinctive competencies with external opportunities and threats
3. Develop or maintain competitive advantage
4. Be funded from a long-term perspective

PRIORITIZING AND SELECTING STRATEGIES

Strategies are the link between objectives and results, and there are typically several options to achieve results. In some cases, a multistrategy option is essential, while other cases demand that a strategy be selected from the options. In practice, a combination of strategies is often used in larger healthcare organizations.

When deciding between strategy alternatives, assumptions underlying each option should be reviewed. Risks inherent to each alternative and corresponding rewards are often the foundation for such review. Decision makers should consider each risk, answering a series of questions:

1. What are the consequences if this strategy is selected?
2. What is the "worst case" scenario for this strategy, and how seriously would that scenario impact the organization?

3. How can risk for this strategy be mitigated?
4. If this strategy is not accepted, what is the impact if a competitor selects this strategy?

Strategy selection is also limited by organizational constraints.

COMMON ORGANIZATIONAL CONSTRAINTS THAT LIMIT STRATEGIES

- *Availability of financial resources*—Funding is scarce and limited, and an organization will not be able to fund all strategies.
- *Attitude toward risk*—A general idea of the level of risk deemed acceptable by the organization can establish a bar for screening alternative strategies.
- *Capabilities of the organization*—Some strategy options may require competencies beyond the scope of the organization.
- *Competitive response*—Selection of a strategy may trigger an aggressive response from competitors in the market.

Risk and limitation analysis can be a useful instrument in screening strategy options that are considered viable by the organization. From the remaining strategy options, leaders can utilize additional tools to assess each option. Three such tools are the growth–share matrix, the possible, implement, challenge, kill (PICK) Chart, and tests that evaluate strategy options.

Growth-Share Matrix

Framing services that the organization offers in terms of growth and profitability can be useful when selecting strategies and allocating resources. A **growth–share matrix**, made popular by Boston Consulting Group (n.d.), allows an organization to analyze its portfolio of products and services relative to market share and market growth rate (see Figure 6.1).

Stars are services/products that have high market share in a fast-growing market. They require significant resources to maintain market share, but can convert to cash cows when market growth slows. If market share declines and market growth slows, stars convert to dogs. **Cash cows** are services/products that have high market share in a slow-growing market. They are typically mature and receive as little investment as possible, but produce cash reserves for the organization. **Question marks** (aka, **problem children)** are services/products with low market share in a fast-growing market. This is typically where a new service/product enters the market, requiring significant investments. Services/products in this quadrant should be analyzed regularly to determine if they should be maintained. **Dogs** are services/products with low market share in a slow-growing market. They do not contribute significantly to net profit, and may even contribute to loss. In the healthcare industry, services/products in this quadrant may be maintained in order to meet the

FIGURE 6.1 Growth-Share Matrix

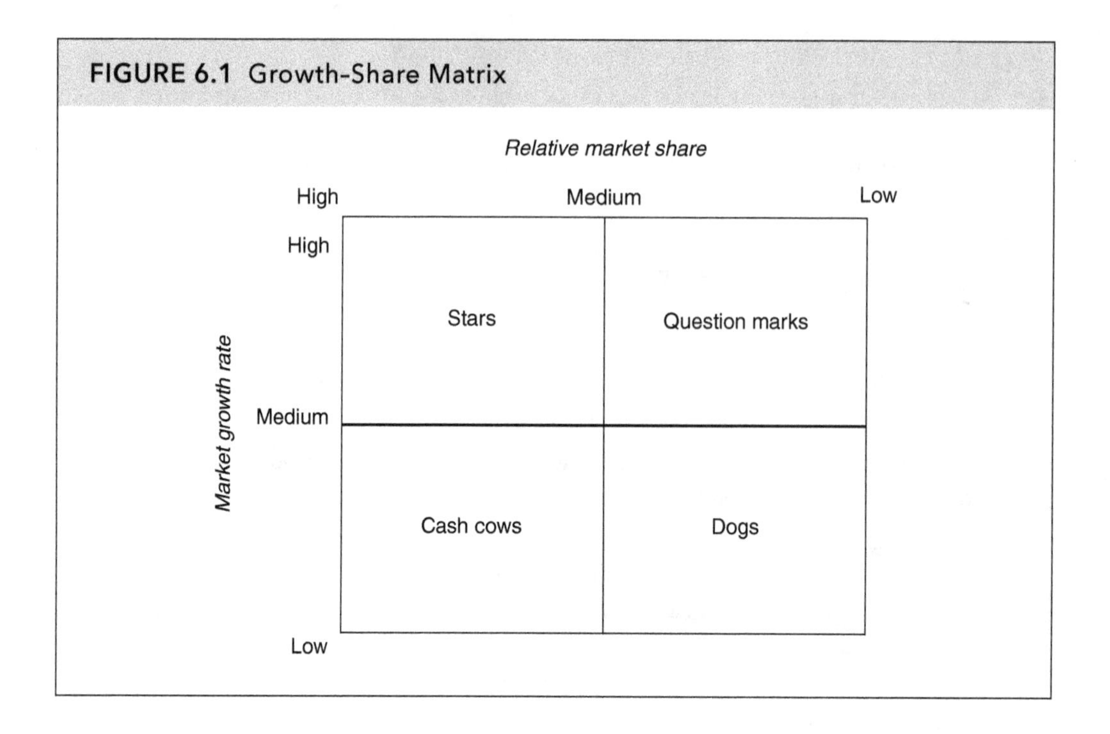

mission of the organization; however, financial pressure exists to divest these services/products.

An example of a portfolio analysis for a large hospital is shown in Figure 6.2. Plastic surgery and behavioral health services have high market share but the growth rate has slowed. These service lines generate excess cash for the organization, which can be used to develop stars and question marks. Service lines such as cardiology and geriatrics are likely highly profitable and should receive resources from the organization that will encourage them to grow into cash cows. Neurology, emergency services, and ambulatory surgery will develop either into stars or dogs. These services require attention, so that those that are likely to develop into stars receive additional resources while those that are likely to develop into dogs are minimized or cut. The pediatrics, ophthalmology, and psychiatry service lines have low growth and low market share and may be targets for reduction. However, the needs of the community and the mission of the organization should drive any decisions for these service lines.

PICK Chart

A **PICK (Possible, Implement, Challenge, Kill) Chart** is used to rank projects on a 2x2 matrix according to their difficulty (cost) versus payoff (benefit) relationship. The PICK Chart is divided into four quadrants, representing four different difficulty/payoff possibilities (Figure 6.3).

The quadrants are:

- Possible—options that are easy to implement but have low payoff expectations

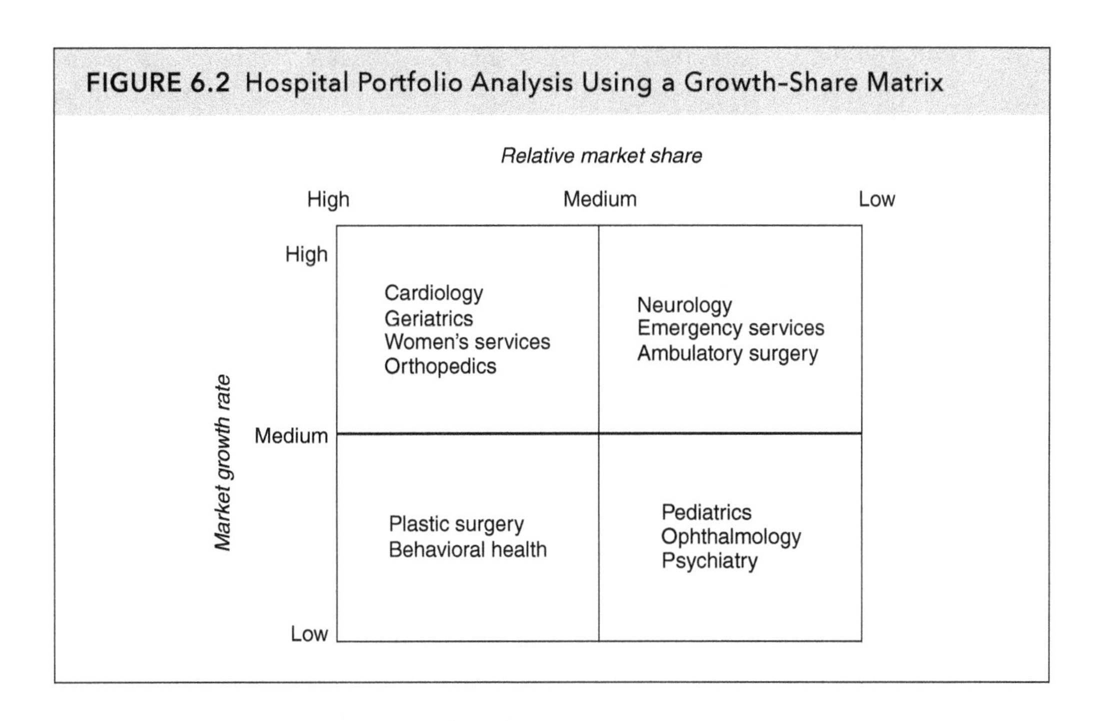

- Implement—options that are easy to implement and have high payoff expectations (ideal)
- Challenge—options that are hard to implement and have high payoff expectations
- Kill—options that are hard to implement and have low payoff expectations

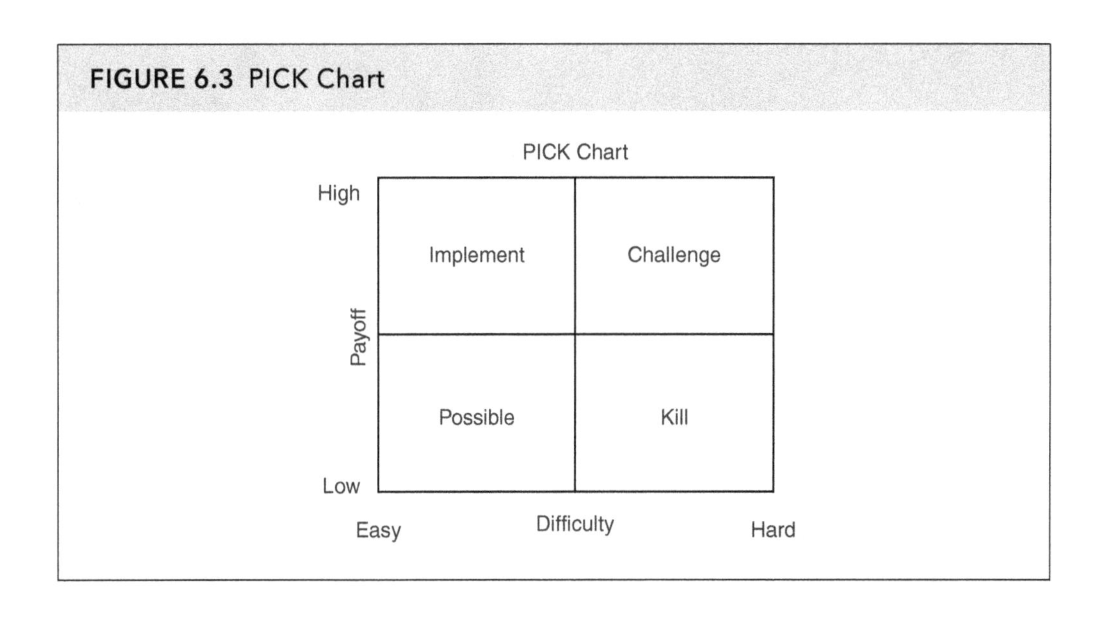

The PICK Chart allows teams to organize which strategy options can be implemented easily with a high payoff (the ideal) and which should not be considered.

The process of determining which quadrant best describes a strategy allows the team to evaluate several impact factors for the strategy, such as:

- Ability to monitor and evaluate outcomes of the strategy
- Influence of strategy outcomes on the organization
- Cost to implement the strategy
- Time requirements for successful implementation
- Staff availability
- Available data
- Ease of gathering data

Evaluation Tests

Three tests can be applied to conduct a comparative evaluation of strategies, and to measure how well a strategy will perform for an organization:

1. The **goodness of fit test** measures how well a strategy is matched with the healthcare organization's internal and external factors (from the environmental assessment).
2. The **competitive advantage test** indicates whether a strategy will lead to a sustainable competitive advantage for the organization. Competitive advantages are considered "superstrengths" and give an organization an edge in the market.
3. The **performance test** evaluates strategy options to determine whether the organization should expect increased performance, ideally in terms of profitability and/or gains in competitive position.

TYPES OF STRATEGIES

Most strategies can be defined as differentiation strategies, focus strategies, or cost leadership strategies.

A **differentiation strategy** is used when the healthcare organization delivers products or services that are distinct in the minds of consumers. The organization relies on brand loyalty to drive consumer decision making. An orthopedic group practice, for example, may be well-known in its market for providing high-quality, compassionate care. An objective to expand into physical therapy and sports medicine services could be supported by a strategy that capitalizes on the practice's reputation—the new services would benefit from a halo effect of the existing service reputation. Patients would receive a continuum of care services through the practice, and the practice would benefit from a new revenue stream.

A **focus strategy** concentrates a single service or grouping of similar services on a specific patient population. The advantage of employing a focus strategy is that the organization can focus on doing one thing very well, with personnel who have distinctive competencies in an area and processes that are efficient. The American Heart Association has a mission of "Building healthier lives, free of cardiovascular disease and stroke." It focuses resources and efforts that target a specific disease category (cardiovascular disease and stroke) to a specific population (those at risk for the disease category).

Organizations that emphasize low cost and efficiency of operations employ a **cost leadership strategy**. Such organizations seek to attract and maintain customers based on low pricing, such as in a competitive contract–bidding environment. Economies of scale in service operations, administration, technology, and other areas are essential elements for a cost leadership strategy. This strategy requires a clear understanding of direct costs at the service level, which is difficult to ascertain, and a minimizing of indirect and administrative costs. Organizations that utilize a cost leadership strategy have low margins, due to lesser reimbursement amounts, and rely on high patient volume to achieve net income targets. While cost leadership can be an effective strategy, some consumers of healthcare services equate low price with low quality. Therefore, applying a cost leadership strategy requires an understanding of the consumer market and the ability to use low cost as a mechanism for driving acceptable price.

A cost leadership strategy is difficult for smaller independent healthcare organizations, and is seen more often in organizations that have integrated delivery models. **Horizontal integration** occurs when providers of similar services combine, either through merger/acquisition or through an alliance. When an organization expands services beyond its current level of provision, **vertical integration** occurs. Examples of horizontal and vertical integration strategies are shown in Figure 6.4. Implementation strategies for horizontal and vertical integration include mergers/acquisitions, joint ventures, and strategic alliances.

Mergers and acquisitions involve two or more organizations, each operating independently, that become a single entity through exchange of ownership. Often, the exchange of ownership is driven by factors that threaten organizational viability, such as market share and profitability. Many rural hospitals, for example, faced a choice of either closing their doors or being acquired by a hospital system. Other drivers include reduction in service duplication and associated inefficiencies, larger volumes of patients, market expansion to greater geographical areas, and improvements in critical operational areas. While mergers/acquisitions have potential benefits, they are difficult to achieve successfully. Two organizations with independent managerial control, autonomy, and different cultures often find it challenging to reach their full potential upon consolidation.

MERGERS AND ACQUISITIONS IN HEALTH CARE

For decades, mergers and acquisitions were seen as the preferred mechanism to achieve scale and bargaining power in the hospital sector. The Patient Protection and Affordable Care Act (ACA) encouraged health systems to move toward population health, which requires a continuum of services across providers. However, the Federal Trade Commission (FTC) has scrutinized mergers and acquisitions among large health systems for their potential anticompetitive effects, leading to increased activity in other strategy areas.

FIGURE 6.4 Examples of Horizontal and Vertical Integration

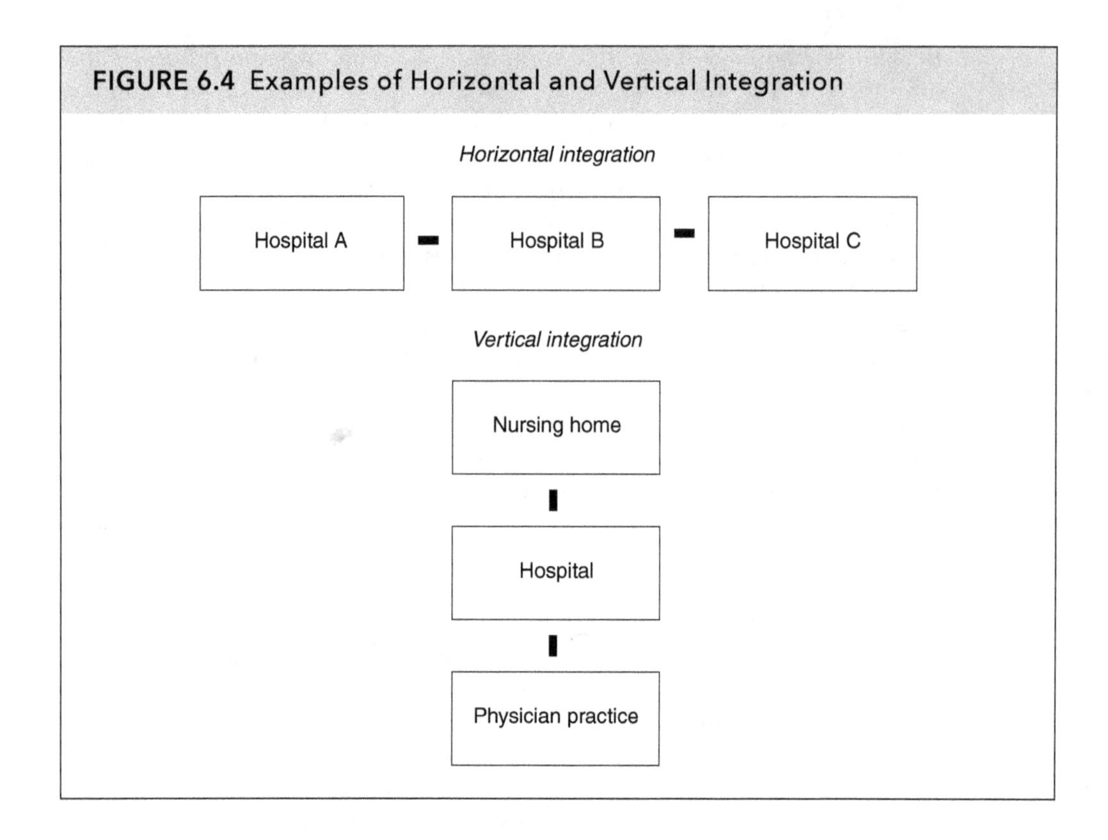

Joint ventures are mutually beneficial formalized collaborations among providers, where two or more healthcare organizations strive to take advantage of strengths and overcome weaknesses. There are several options in establishing partnerships, including affiliating through management services and through contractual services. Physician groups that want to maintain their independence but remove the burden of administrative overhead may be inclined to form a partnership through management services. When the goal is improved efficiency and increased negotiating power, providers are likely to enter into contractual services. Three common contractual arrangements are physician–hospital organization (PHO), professional service agreement (PSA), and independent physician association (IPA).

A **PHO** is a legal entity formed by a hospital and one or more physicians/physician groups and serves as a negotiating and contracting unit on behalf of the member hospital and physicians. PHOs negotiate fee schedules with payers and present the fee schedule to members, who can accept or reject individually. A **PSA** is a financial relationship between a hospital and physician practice, where the hospital and practice remain autonomous. The hospital manages the administrative side of the practice and compensates physicians on a fair market basis. This relationship is often the first step toward hospital acquisition of the practice. In an **IPA**, physician practices (both hospital-owned and private/independent) gain the benefit of an independent organization that can negotiate network-based contracts and performance incentive programs. IPAs are typically open to both primary care and specialty care physician practices.

Strategic alliances are loose relationships among providers to achieve common goals. There is no exchange of ownership or loss of autonomy by any of the participants, and contracts are commonly utilized. The advantage of strategic alliances is to combine resources for purchasing power and/or economies of scale.

STRATEGIC ALLIANCE EXAMPLE–VIZIENT, INC.

Vizient, Inc. was formed by a merger of Voluntary Hospitals of American, Inc. and University Health System Consortium. Vizient provides purchasing discounts, access to consultants, job recruiting services, and other benefits to its members (www.vizientinc.com).

Accountable Care Organizations (ACOs) are groups of hospitals, physicians, and other healthcare providers that partner to provide high-quality care to patients. ACOs are encouraged under the ACA to form for the purpose of providing coordinated services to the Medicare population. Providers have financial incentives, including rewards for meeting specific clinical targets and total cost of care benchmarks, and make more revenue if they keep their patients healthy. On the private side, providers and insurers can collaborate in an ACO model. While designed to reward better (versus more) care, some economists are concerned that ACOs have also driven consolidation in the healthcare industry.

OPERATIONAL PLANS

After strategies are established for objectives, it is time to develop operational or action plans. This is the "doing" stage, where leaders hire, fire, build, advertise, and so on according to the strategies that are outlined. Detailed plans should be developed for each of the areas used to support the overall strategy: service delivery operations, communications, staffing, and finance. The **service delivery operations plan** identifies exactly which services will be provided to specific groups, and the exact nature of those services. For example, if a home health agency decides to expand services, it will need to specifically identify which services will be offered and to which patient population. The **communications plan** provides messaging about programs, including time and location, to potential patients, providers, and staff. For example, a rehabilitation center would need a plan that covered three elements: informing individuals and groups about the organization, persuading individuals that services are beneficial, and reminding individuals and groups about the service capabilities of the program.

The **staffing plan** identifies who will carry out the activities indicated in each strategy. The plan should consider what professionals will be needed to deliver services, whether part-time staff or contractors can be used, and the availability of personnel with the proper credentials outside of the organization. The **finance plan** is presented as a budget, which indicates the financial resources required to execute the plan. The budgeting process is often a point where objectives are reprioritized, as a lack of financial support requires adjustments to objectives. As a result, there is constant back-and-forth between the budget and the strategic plan. Other plans that support the strategic plan include a marketing plan, capital plan, and master facilities plan.

IMPLEMENTING STRATEGY IN THE HEALTH SETTING

Healthcare organizations can develop several different strategies to support objectives and may implement different strategies simultaneously or as part of a structured sequence. In other cases, multiple strategies must be evaluated in order to make the decision regarding which strategy or strategies to implement. And once strategies have been implemented, they must be monitored over time. Recall that strategic planning is a "living" process, meaning that updates to strategies and replacement strategies are likely to be necessary.

A helpful tool to track implementation plans is to develop an implementation framework (Table 6.1). The implementation framework can include additional information that is helpful in executing the strategic plan, such as external stakeholder involvement, approval levels, and additional team members required for success. The identified responsible leader will often pull together an implementation team. These teams should be broad and include middle-level managers and supervisors who understand the strategic planning process, as well as direction from the board and CEO.

TABLE 6.1 Basic Implementation Framework

	Resource Requirements	Target Completion	Responsibility
Key Area 1	Scale	Month/year	Leader
Objective 1.1 a. Strategy 1 b. Strategy 2 c. Strategy 3			
Objective 1.2 a. Strategy 1 b. Strategy 2 c. Strategy 3			
Objective 1.3 a. Strategy 1 b. Strategy 2 c. Strategy 3			

It is crucial that momentum from the strategic planning process not be lost and that implementation teams begin work as quickly as possible. Top-down leadership is critical at this point. As Peter F. Drucker once said, "Plans are only good intentions unless they immediately degenerate into hard work."

FAILING TO IMPLEMENT STRATEGY

Organizations that experience failure at the point of implementation typically suffer one or more of three causes:

1. *Loss of energy*. Strategic planning is enabled at the highest level of the organization, consumes large amounts of resources, and is highly visible within the organization and in the community. Once the plan has been written, it is easy for employees at all levels to sit back and relax, having undertaken a mammoth exercise. Implementation is a much less visible task, and loss of energy can be accompanied by a lack of focus.
2. *View the implementation as an "add-on" to normal operations*. Employees can view implementation as an addition to duties that distracts them from their operational activities.
3. *Lack of leadership*. While development of the strategic plan receives high levels of attention from senior and other managers, a lack of management at the implementation phase will lead to failure.

Given the significant resources that are committed to the strategic planning process and the importance of implementation to the success of the organization (recall the tie to the mission), a management approach to implementation should be put in place. This approach must have an overall leader and regular review periods to evaluate progress. The plan must be driven down to the operational (day-to-day) activities of the organization and communicated on a regular basis to employees and stakeholders. Organizations should consider leadership skills within the organization relative to the implementation activities, and seek talent outside when there are gaps. If 5% to 10% of employees have the skills to lead the implementation, the remaining 90% to 95% of employees will follow their lead. Evaluation and progress review are discussed in Chapter 7.

SETTING A BUDGET

As noted earlier, a main limitation in strategy selection and implementation is the availability of financial resources to fund the strategy. While the strategic plan lays out the direction of the organization and the objectives it intends to complete toward achieving its mission, the **budget** is a plan for how resources (commonly money) will be used to support the objectives. The challenge of aligning the organization's budget with the strategic plan is that selected strategies carry associated implementation costs, which drive the budget, while strategy selection is dependent, at least in part, on the availability of organizational resources. So, how do you solve this chicken-or-egg dilemma? Two options are as follows:

1. Prepare a draft operating budget and update it after the strategic plan has been completed. This option allows for all costs related to strategic initiatives to be included in the annual budget for each year. It also allows for the impact of strategies on the budget to be considered in the strategy development and selection process.
2. Conduct the strategic planning process before beginning the budget process and use results of the strategic plan to inform the budget. This option includes risk that strategy options selected may not be financially feasible for the organization. The advantage is that a budget can be built that is consistent with the strategic direction of the organization, including operational forecasts that arose from the planning process.

Regardless of the method used, having clear connections between the budget, organizational cash flow, and the strategic plan allow leaders to make spending decisions in the short term that lead to strategic success. Therefore, it is imperative that strategies identify budget amounts for any additional operating and capital expenses.

A budget formalizes activities between departments/units while aligning those activities to the strategic plan. It also provides the assignment of decision-making responsibilities, enhances manager accountability, and provides a basis for managerial performance evaluation. Finally, a budget encourages efficiency within departments/units, which leads to overall organizational efficiency.

THE BUDGET PROCESS

Participation in the budgeting process is an important part of communication between employees and management, leading to acceptance of budget goals and restrictions. When used as a basis for performance evaluation, the budget must be considered fair and reasonable. The process of creating the budget with employee input at different levels within the organization leads to buy-in and greater chances of success. Creating budgets that are effective can be enhanced by:

1. Identifying decision makers across the organization and involving them throughout the budget process
2. Using technology to coordinate budgeting efforts for team members
3. Mirroring the strategic plan in the budget
4. Monitoring the budget and including team members in comparing budgeted expenses to actual expenses
5. Identifying issues quickly and developing plans for resolution

Keep in mind that a budget is a tool that translates the organization's objectives and strategies into dollar amounts. When developed well, it can provide opportunities for employees to work together as a team and to keep the organization on the path toward strategic success.

CASE STUDY MEMORIAL HOSPITAL, INC.

The mission of Memorial Hospital, Inc. is to provide compassionate, accessible, high-quality, cost-effective healthcare to the community, and to promote health.

The strategic planning committee met several times to discuss each of the objectives previously identified, brainstorming strategy options for each. At the direction of the chief financial officer (CFO), the committee did not consider financial resource constraints as a limitation at this point. After listing all strategy options, the committee completed a growth–share matrix and PICK Chart to analyze options. The analyses also included evaluation tests to ensure that selected strategies would be effective for the organization.

The strategies identified for Objective 1.1 are listed as an example in the following implementation framework:

	Resource Requirements	Target Completion	Responsibility
Key Area 1: Economy Increase in the number of privately insured citizens affords an opportunity to increase private pay revenues. Five counties have been identified with the greatest potential for increasing hospital revenue. The hospital realizes its greatest margin (revenues less expenses) from private health insurance payers.			Chief operating officer
Objective 1.1: To increase private insurance patient revenues in the five identified (based on growth of privately insured population) counties by 5% in the next 12 months, by targeting the five counties with advertising and physician relations campaigns.			

(continued)

CASE STUDY MEMORIAL HOSPITAL, INC. (*continued*)

a. Strategy 1.1a: Develop and implement a comprehensive marketing plan targeting the five counties.	$300,000	July 1, 20XX	Director, Planning and Marketing
b. Strategy 1.1b: Work with Physician Relations to continue building physician relationships in the five counties and increase referrals.	$25,000	July 1, 20XX	Director, Physician Relations

The following strategy development worksheet will aid you in developing strategies for your healthcare organization's operations.

STRATEGY DEVELOPMENT WORKSHEET

Answer These Questions First

1. What are the distinctive competencies of your healthcare organization? What do you do well that makes you different from other healthcare organizations?

____

____

____

____

2. What market segment or segments should you select to match your organization's skills and resources and your constituents' needs in those segments?

____

____

____

____

3. Do you have the skill/resources to pursue several segments or should you concentrate on one segment? Is the revenue potential for that segment large enough to sustain your organization and allow for growth?

Now Develop Your Positioning Statement

1. Distinctive Competencies

2. Patient/Client Segments Sought

3. Services to Be Offered

4. Need/Demand for Services

5. Revenue-Generating Potential

____

____

6. Growth Potential

____

____

____

____

Next Develop Your Overall Strategy (Growth, Stability, Retrenchment) for Each Major Program: Growth (Add or Expand Spectrum of Programs)

Growth: Alternative Strategy 1

Pros

1. ____
2. ____
3. ____

Cons

1. ____
2. ____
3. ____

Growth: Alternative Strategy 2

Pros

1. ____
2. ____
3. ____

Cons

1. ____
2. ____
3. ____

Stability (Keep Same Programs While Improving on Effectiveness and Efficiency)

Stability: Alternative Strategy 1

Pros

1. ____

2. ______________________________

3. ______________________________

Cons

1. ______________________________

2. ______________________________

3. ______________________________

Stability: Alternative Strategy 2

Pros

1. ______________________________

2. ______________________________

3. ______________________________

Cons

1. ______________________________

2. ______________________________

3. ______________________________

Retrenchment (Major Reduction or Elimination in Existing Programs or Locations)

Retrenchment: Alternative Strategy 1

Pros

1. ______________________________

2. ______________________________

3. ______________________________

Cons

1. ______________________________

2. ______________________________

3. ______________________________

Retrenchment: Alternative Strategy 2

Pros

1. ______________________________

2. ______________________________

3. ______________________________

Cons

1. ______________________________

2. ______________________________

3. ______________________________

Recommended Overall Strategy for Each Program

Justification: Explain why this is the best alternative.

Pros

1. ______________________________

2. ______________________________

3. ______________________________

Cons

1. ______________________________

2. ______________________________

3. ______________________________

Finally, Establish Operational Strategies for Each Key Result Area Objective in Each Major Program That Supports Your Overall Strategy for That Program

An action plan for each key result area should be developed. The action plan establishes coordinated linkages among objectives, strategies, and operational plans and helps you develop the interrelationships among plans at each organizational level. It helps goals come to life with appropriate action.

Action Plan

OBJECTIVE:

____

____

____

____

STRATEGIES:

A. ______________________________

____

____

____

B. ______________________________

____

____

____

C. ____

____

____

____

D. ____

____

____

____

E. ____

____

____

____

Action Plan	Person Responsible	Date Started	Date Completed

GLOSSARY OF TERMS

Accountable Care Organizations (ACOs)—groups of hospitals, physicians, and other healthcare providers that partner to provide high-quality care to patients

Budget—a plan for how resources (commonly money) will be used to support objectives

Cash cows—in a growth–share matrix model, services/products that have high market share in a slow-growing market

Communications plan—provides messaging about programs, including time and location, to potential patients, providers, and staff

Competitive advantage test—an evaluation test that indicates whether a strategy will lead to a sustainable competitive advantage for the organization; competitive advantages are considered "superstrengths" and give an organization an edge in the market

Cost leadership strategy—an organization emphasizes low cost and efficiency of operations

Differentiation strategy—an organization delivers products or services that are distinct in the minds of consumers

Dogs—in a growth–share matrix model, services/products with low market share in a slow-growing market

Finance plan—financial resources required to execute the plan

Focus strategy—concentrates a single service or grouping of similar services on a specific patient population

Goodness of fit test—an evaluation test that measures how well a strategy is matched with the healthcare organization's internal and external factors (from the environmental assessment)

Growth–share matrix—a method that allows an organization to analyze its portfolio of business or products relative to market share and market growth rate

Horizontal integration—combination of providers of similar services

Independent physician association (IPA)—an arrangement where physician practices (both hospital-owned and private/independent) gain the benefit of an independent organization that can negotiate network-based contracts and performance incentive programs

Joint ventures—mutually beneficial formalized collaborations among providers, where two or more healthcare organizations strive to take advantage of strengths and overcome weaknesses

Mergers and acquisitions—two or more organizations, each operating independently, become a single entity through exchange of ownership

Performance test—an evaluation test that assesses strategy options to determine whether the organization should expect increased performance, ideally in terms of profitability and/or gains in competitive position

Physician–hospital organization (PHO)—a legal entity formed by a hospital and one or more physicians/physician groups and serves as a negotiating and contracting unit on behalf of the member hospital and physicians

PICK (Possible, Implement, Challenge, Kill) Chart—a methodology used to rank projects on a 2x2 matrix according to their difficulty (cost) versus payoff (benefit) relationship

Professional service agreement (PSA)—a financial relationship between a hospital and physician practice, where the hospital and practice remain autonomous

Question marks (problem children)—in a growth–share matrix model, services/products with low market share in a fast-growing market

Service delivery operations plan—identifies exactly which services will be provided to specific groups, and the exact nature of those services

Staffing plan—identifies who will carry out the activities indicated in each strategy

Stars—in a growth–share matrix model, services/products that have high market share in a fast-growing market

Strategic alliances—loose relationships among providers to achieve common goals

Strategy—the course of action an organization takes to complete its objective; it is the link between objectives and results

Vertical integration—expansion of services beyond the provider's current level of provision

REFERENCE

Boston Consulting Group. (n.d.). Our history of shaping the future. Retrieved from https://www.bcg.com/about/heritage/default.aspx

CHAPTER 7

EVALUATION AND CONTROL

It is a bad plan that admits no modification.

—Publilius Syrus
Latin writer (85–43 BCE)

LEARNING OBJECTIVES

1. Understand why evaluating and adapting strategy is essential to success.
2. Conduct an analysis of services provided by quarter.
3. Describe financial ratios that can be used to evaluate performance against expectations.
4. Apply the plan-do-study-act (PDSA) cycle to process improvement.
5. Use a balanced scorecard and key performance indicators (KPIs) to assess progress toward objectives.

In the "old days," taking a long trip by car involved a road map. The starting point and destination were identified on the map, the best route was determined, and the trip begun. In strategic planning, the destination is the objective, the route is the strategy, and the departure is the implementation of the strategy. As the trip progressed, drivers would look to highway signs for feedback as to progress toward their destination. This feedback was essential, as a sign could alert drivers if they made a wrong turn. The process of continuous feedback allowed for modifications, if a wrong turn occurred, and getting back on track as quickly as possible. Now, imagine if there were no road signs to let drivers know if they were on the correct road. By the time it was realized that an error had been made, it may have been too late to continue the trip. Unfortunately, many healthcare organizations fail to analyze results to see if objectives are being met, leading to less than optimal performance.

■ ■ ■

INTEGRATION OF PLANNING AND CONTROL

As discussed in Chapter 2, evaluation and control should be a natural progression in developing a strategic plan. Planning is a process that relies on feedback of results, which reflects the organization's ability to complete its objectives and reach its mission. As such, evaluation and control are integrated into the planning model through a planning and control process (Figure 7.1), which begins with the overall planning process. As strategies are implemented, results are produced, such as number of services rendered, amount of revenue generated, and types of behaviors altered. Information on results can be used to evaluate whether the results indicate if the objective will be (or has been) met. The performance evaluation of strategies for each objective identifies areas that need adjustments in activities, resources, and/or people. These decisions then alter the plan for the purpose of achieving the objectives, allowing a new cycle to begin. As you can see, the flow of information from results is crucial to good evaluation.

The last stage of the planning process is to determine progress toward completion of objectives.

FIGURE 7.1 Planning and Control Process

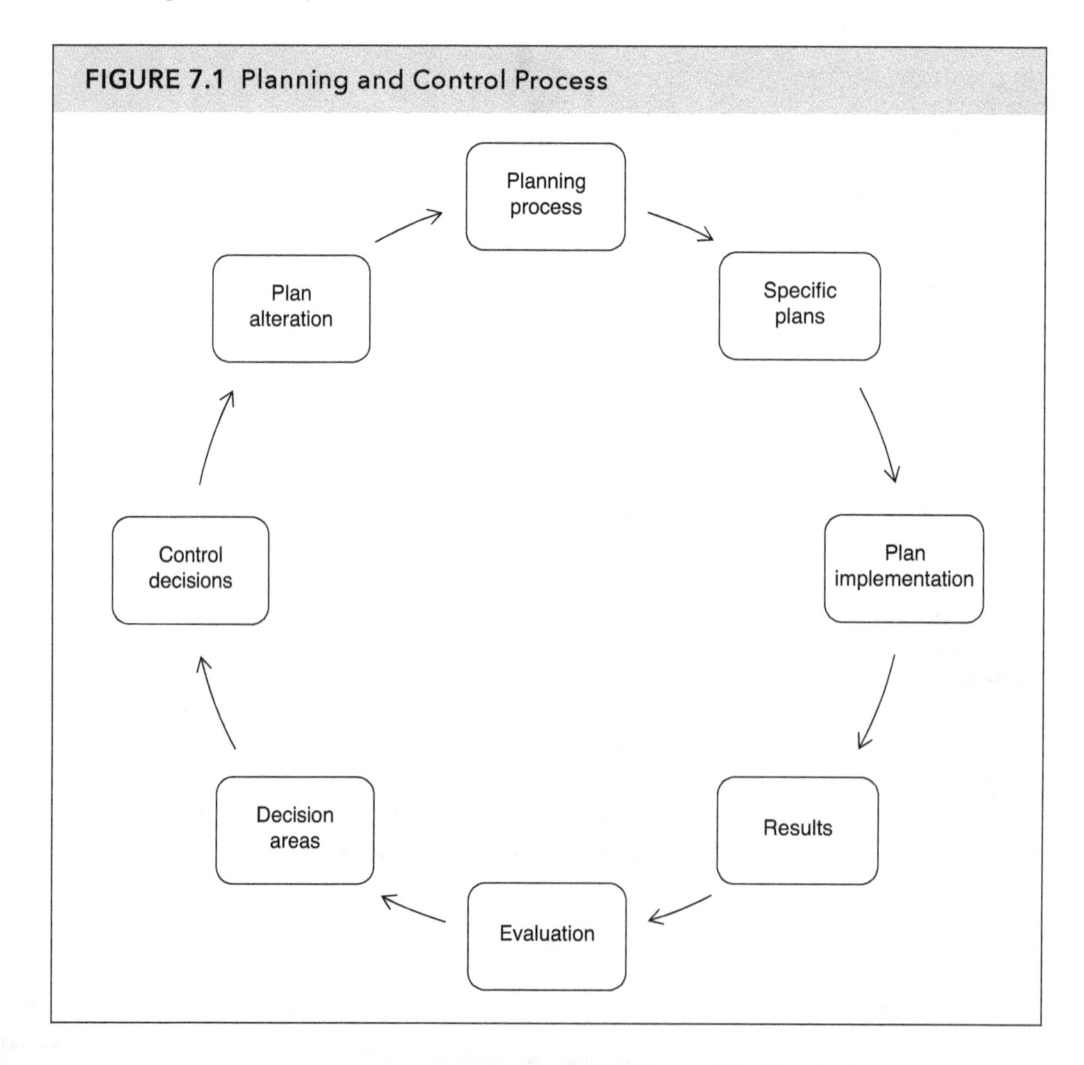

QUESTIONS THAT CAN GUIDE THE REVIEW PROCESS

- What is the gap between targets and actual performance?
- Have the objectives been accomplished?
- Which objectives were accomplished; was progress made toward achieving the broader plan and organizational mission?
- Have additional internal strengths and/or weaknesses been revealed?
- Has something in the environment changed that affects objectives?

Timing of information is also an important consideration. Strategic plans are long-term plans; however, they are implemented through a series of short- and intermediate-term operational plans. Executive management should not wait until the strategic plan time period has run its course before reviewing control information. In practice, there is a balance between allowing enough time for results to accrue and evaluating results quickly enough to make changes that will increase the chance that objectives are met. Most healthcare organizations can control operations with monthly or quarterly reports, depending on the objectives. These reports can be rolled up into annual reports that become the feedback necessary to control the plan.

PERFORMANCE EVALUATION AND CONTROL

A healthcare organization should evaluate performance in each of the key areas, assessing results and the causes of those results. Three key control areas that should be evaluated are services provided, revenues generated, and patient/client attitudes. **Evaluation and control of services provided** includes an assessment of budgeted/projected services provided versus actual services provided. For a home health agency, a quarterly report of services provided might look like Table 7.1. From this table, leadership can determine which visits by provider type are performing above or below the respective projected (budgeted) amount. The performance index is a quick reference for this purpose, with an index near 1.00 indicating that actual performance is comparable to projected performance, an index above 1.00 representing actual performance above projected performance, and an index below 1.00 expressing actual performance below projected performance.

Performance indices are particularly useful when there are large numbers of programs or services being evaluated.

Several tools are used to establish **revenue/cost control** procedures, such as budgets, expense ratios, and activity cost analysis. **Budgets** are commonly used in healthcare organizations for both planning and control of revenues and expenses, and are typically established by using historical percentages of various expenses as a percentage of revenues. Once the total level of expected revenue is determined, expense items can be budgeted as a percentage of that total revenue. If the healthcare organization uses zero-based budgeting, where each budget is developed "from scratch" without influence from the

TABLE 7.1 Report of Visits by Provider Type–Q1

Provider	(A) Projected Visits	(B) Actual Visits	(C) Variation	(C / A) % Variation	(B / A) Performance Index
RNs	330	377	+47	+14.2	1.14
LPNs	562	614	+52	+9.3	1.09
NAs	844	683	−161	−19.1	0.81
PTs	264	268	+4	+1.5	1.02
Total	2,000	1,942			

LPN, licensed practical nurse; NA, nursing assistant; PT, physical therapist.

previous period's budget, expenditures for each objective must be estimated. These estimates, calculated over an annual period, then become the budgeted expenses for the next year. Annual expenses can be broken down into quarterly and monthly expenses, which become the standard for comparison of actual expenses. The same type of analysis used to monitor visits by provider type can be used to analyze data on revenues and expenses.

A local hospital and physician group opens a new service provider, Tri-Cities Geriatric Center. They set objectives and strategies, which drive a revenue and expense budget for the center. After the end of the first year, a budget and variance analysis for the previous year (Table 7.2) shows that, while the actual number of patient visits and associated revenue exceeded budget, net profit (revenues minus expenses) was below budget and the center incurred a loss. A review of expenses shows that expense control was an issue for the center and should be addressed by management.

Historical trend data should be considered when determining the distribution of annual revenues and expenses on a monthly basis. For example, a physician practice with historical annual revenues of $1,500,000 would not want to allocate $125,000 in revenue for each month ($1,500,000/12) if 20% of revenues are historically generated in the first 2 months of the year. If that were the case, the budget for the next year should allocate 20% of revenues—$300,000—across the first 2 months of the year ($150,000 per month), and allocate 80% of revenues—$1,200,000—across the remaining 10 months ($120,000 per month). Similarly, expenses per month that are expected to be greater than or less than the average of the annual total expenses should be allocated accordingly.

Healthcare organizations can also use **financial ratios** to evaluate performance against expectations, against historical trends, and against the industry. Financial ratio analysis combines values from financial statements (income statement, balance sheet, and statement of cash flows) to create single numbers that have easily interpretable economic significance and that facilitate comparison.

Financial ratios that are commonly used for analysis are listed in Table 7.3.

TABLE 7.2 Tri-Cities Geriatric Center: Budget Variance Report

	Budgeted	Actual	Variance	% Variance
Number of visits	12,363	14,100	1,737	14.05%
Private insurance visits	9,891	11,300	1,409	14.25%
Medicaid visits	2,472	2,800	328	13.27%
Net revenue	$568,721	$598,100	$29,379	5.17%
Private revenue	$494,547	$508,500	$13,954	2.82%
Medicaid revenue	$74,174	$89,600	$15,426	20.80%
Expenses				
Salaries and wages	$139,020	$147,835	$8,815	6.34%
Physician fees	$184,950	$201,334	$16,384	8.86%
Malpractice insurance	$32,983	$34,686	$1,703	5.16%
Travel and education	$4,624	$3,700	($924)	−19.98%
General insurance	$8,631	$8,824	$193	2.23%
Utilities	$12,638	$12,267	($371)	-2.94%
Equipment and lease	$1,541	$1,672	$131	8.48%
Other operating expenses	$92,475	$107,385	$14,910	16.12%
Total operating expenses	$476,862	$517,703	$40,841	8.56%
Net profit (loss)	$91,858	$80,397	($11,461)	−12.48%

CATEGORIES OF FINANCIAL RATIOS TYPICALLY REVIEWED IN FINANCIAL ANALYSIS

1. *Profitability ratios*—Is the organization generating sufficient profits (excess revenues over expenses)?
2. *Liquidity ratios*—Can the organization meet its cash obligations?
3. *Debt management ratios*—Is the organization using the right mix of debt and equity financing?
4. *Asset management ratios*—Does the organization have the right amount of assets for its volume?

TABLE 7.3 Common Financial Ratios

Ratio	Formula	Definition
Profitability Ratios		
Total (profit) margin ratio	Net income divided by total revenues	Measures ability to control expenses
Operating margin ratio	Net operating income divided by operating revenues	Measures ability to control operating expenses
Return on assets ratio	Net income divided by total assets	Measures ability of assets to generate profits
Return on equity ratio	Net income divided by total equity	Measures ability of equity to generate profits
Liquidity Ratios		
Current ratio	Current assets divided by current liabilities	Measures ability to pay current liabilities using current assets
Days cash on hand	Cash and short-term investments divided by daily cash expenses	Measures number of days operations can continue without new revenue
Debt Management Ratios		
Debt ratio	Total liabilities divided by total assets	Measures proportion of debt in total financing
Times interest earned	Earnings before interest and taxes divided by interest expense	Measures dollars of accounting income available to pay each dollar of interest expense
Asset Management Ratios		
Fixed asset turnover ratio	Total revenues divided by net fixed assets	Measures dollars of revenue per dollar of fixed assets
Total asset turnover ratio	Total revenues divided by total assets	Measures dollars of revenue per dollar of total assets
Average collection period	Net accounts receivable divided by daily patient revenue	Measures average number of days it takes to collect receivables

The final key area of control is **patient/client feedback**, which evaluates concerns of those the organization serves. Every healthcare organization should want the people it serves to become aware of its services, programs, and distinctive competencies; to understand how the organization can meet their specific needs; and to have patients/clients who value the organization's services. If these are incorporated into specific, measurable, achievable, relevant, and time-bound (SMART) objectives, as they should be, these objectives become the standard by which current patient/client feedback can be compared. Collecting data about patients/clients should be completed on a regular basis, with a goal of collecting data longitudinally over time so that satisfaction, awareness, and attitudes and behaviors can be compared. Most healthcare organizations use surveys to collect patient/client data.

ESTABLISHING PROCEDURES

Performance evaluation is necessary to ensure that organizational activities are aligned with the strategic plan. Evaluation activities cannot be completed without the data required for analysis, and data collection is driven by management commitment and funding. Therefore, administrators must support data collection and reporting procedures in order to ensure that data-driven corrective action can be taken as part of the evaluation process.

FOUR REASONS TO CONDUCT REGULAR, ONGOING REVIEW OF PROGRESS

1. To encourage and motivate employees and stakeholders
2. To ensure that appropriate progress is being made and that priorities are given attention
3. To identify and resolve problems
4. To reallocate scarce resources to areas most in need

Regular meetings of senior management and the board, with updates from the strategic planning committee, should be part of an organization's formal evaluation process. In addition to status updates, these meetings can be used to ensure that senior management provides support and encouragement for the implementation process. The frequency of these meetings is typically heavy in the first year of plan implementation, with tapering occurring in later years.

Individual performance reviews are another mechanism to enhance plan implementation. Action plan objectives should be built into expectations for personnel, which can then be evaluated formally during the annual performance review process. However, the best practice is to conduct informal evaluations of employee performance on an ongoing basis, which also allows for necessary adjustments to action plans.

The control system in general should:

1. Be linked to strategy
2. Be simple and economical to use
3. Measure both activities and results
4. Flag exceptions
5. Focus on success factors, not trivia
6. Be timely
7. Be flexible, as strategy changes with environmental demands
8. Be reality-based, where written reports are augmented by face-to-face feedback

Strategic planning will not work well without performance evaluation. The evaluation and control stage is where healthcare organizations can see significant benefits from the strategic planning process. When people across the organization and external stakeholders know that progress is being made toward fulfilling the organization's mission, it creates a sense of accomplishment and excitement.

Rewards are also important motivators in a project as large and far-reaching as a strategic plan. Rewards on the individual and group level can be financial, but they can also be nonfinancial. Kickoff parties, major milestone celebrations, contests, employee recognition, and other types of rewards can be used to keep employees and teams motivated and encourage progress.

MONITORING AND IMPLEMENTATION TOOLS

> Not everything that counts can be counted. And not everything that can be counted, counts.
>
> —*Albert Einstein*
> *Theoretical physicist*

Several tools can be used to monitor implementation of the strategic plan. Four common tools are plan–do–study–act (PDSA), Pareto chart, run chart, and the balanced scorecard.

PDSA Cycle

We discussed the **PDSA cycle** (Figure 7.2) in Chapter 2 as a problem-solving process used for quality improvement initiatives. However, it can also be applied to processes. Recall that the PDSA steps include planning an intervention (**plan**), pilot-testing the change on a small scale (**do**), observing and measuring results of the change (**study**), and using knowledge gained to plan for the next steps (**act**).

This is a continuous process of evaluation and feedback to improve the implementation of the strategies and action plans.

A pharmacy develops an objective of increasing its prescription filling business by 20% from a neighborhood in its target market by implementing an

FIGURE 7.2 The Plan-Do-Study-Act (PDSA) Model

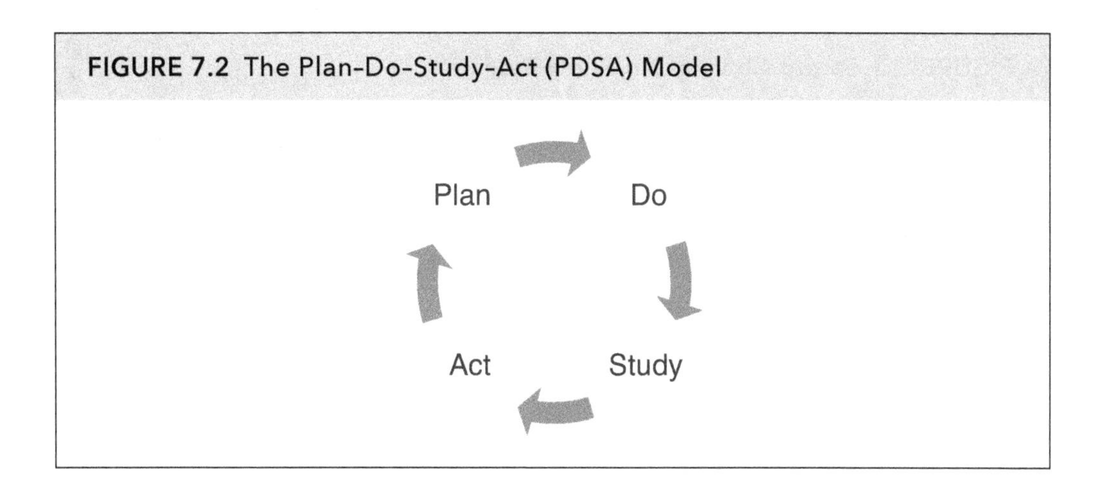

advertising strategy (**plan**). The pharmacy works with an advertising agency to develop and distribute flyers via mailing (**do**) and reviews its database for addresses of patients. The data indicate that there has been a modest increase (3.5%) in patients from the targeted neighborhood (**study**). The pharmacy manager determines that the campaign is not worth the expense and does not renew the activity (**act**).

Pareto Chart

A **Pareto chart** (aka, **Pareto diagram**) is a quality improvement tool that is used to identify factors that contribute to a project or process, allowing a team to concentrate on those factors that have the greatest impact. Vilfredo Pareto was an Italian economist who came up with what is known as the "80/20" rule, meaning that roughly 20% of inputs or activities are responsible for 80% of outcomes or results. The Pareto chart (Figure 7.3) uses two Y axes, with the left-hand Y axis being the count (or frequency) and the right-hand Y axis being the cumulative frequency. Count data are presented in bar chart format, and frequency data are reported as a line.

Consider an example of a primary care clinic that is concerned with no-show rates (patients who fail to arrive for their scheduled appointment) among its Medicaid population. The clinic contacts clients who miss appointments over a 6-month period, and compiles a list of reasons given by the clients. Using Microsoft Excel, the practice manager creates a Pareto chart.

The chart indicates that three reasons account for over 80% of the reasons given for missed appointments: no transportation, no child care, and work conflicts. The practice manager can now work with staff and others to determine if any actions can be taken to mitigate the reasons for patients missing appointments.

Run Chart

A **run chart** graphs data over time and is used to assess change. Take, for example, a clinical unit that is having difficulty with cross-contamination. Lack of proper handwashing is identified as a potential significant reason, and

FIGURE 7.3 Pareto Chart of No-Show Rates

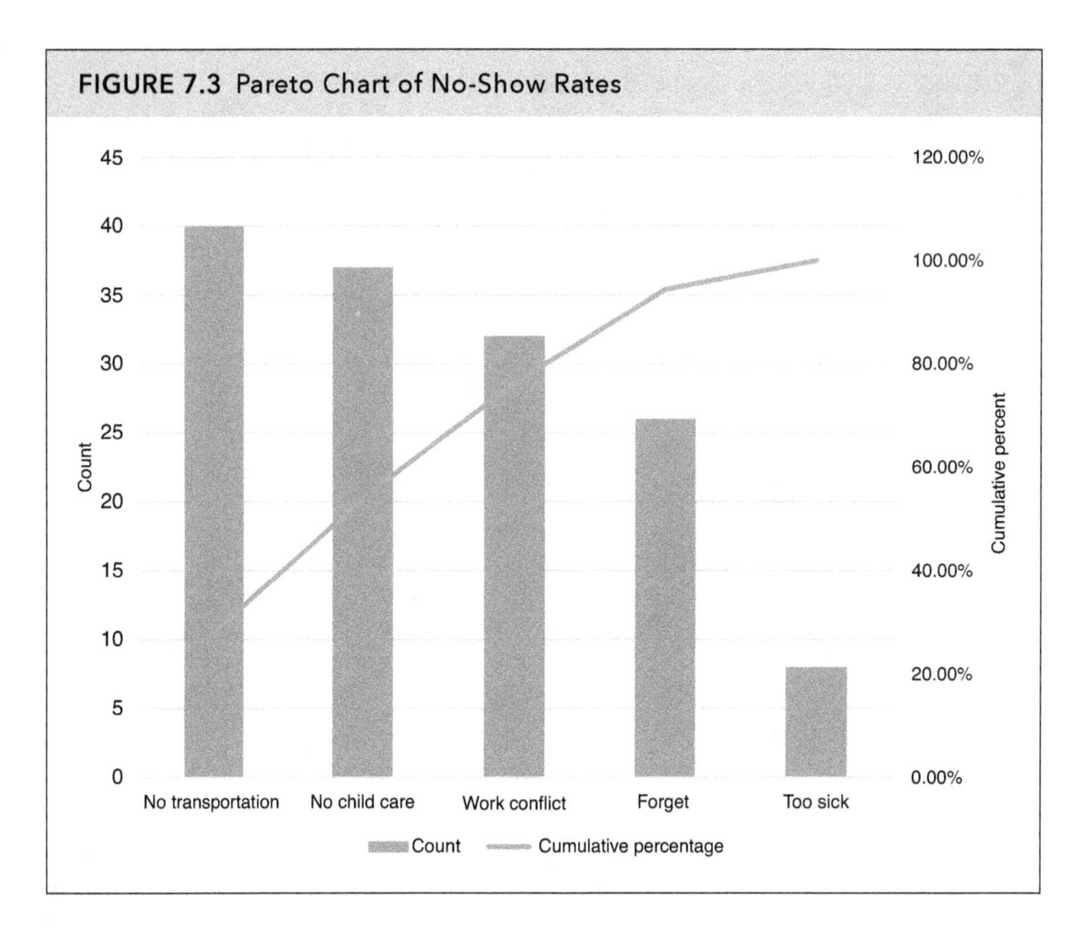

a study is designed where the unit manager conducts an observational study at random times. After 14 weeks of data collection, the unit manager determines that a handwashing policy is necessary, develops the policy, and implements the policy with staff training. She collects data over a total of 6 months and plots the values on a run chart (Figure 7.4). The heavy line below 60% is the median of the compliant observations during that study period. The dotted line at the top is the goal set at week 15, when the policy was implemented.

Run charts are simple to develop and implement.

BENEFITS OF RUN CHARTS

- Easy to use and interpret
- Can be used to determine if change is needed
- Shows results of implemented change
- Can be used to see if improvements are being maintained

Displaying data via a run chart is often followed by a more complex control chart, which considers expected (common cause) variation and outside (special cause) variation.

FIGURE 7.4 Run Chart of Compliance With Policy

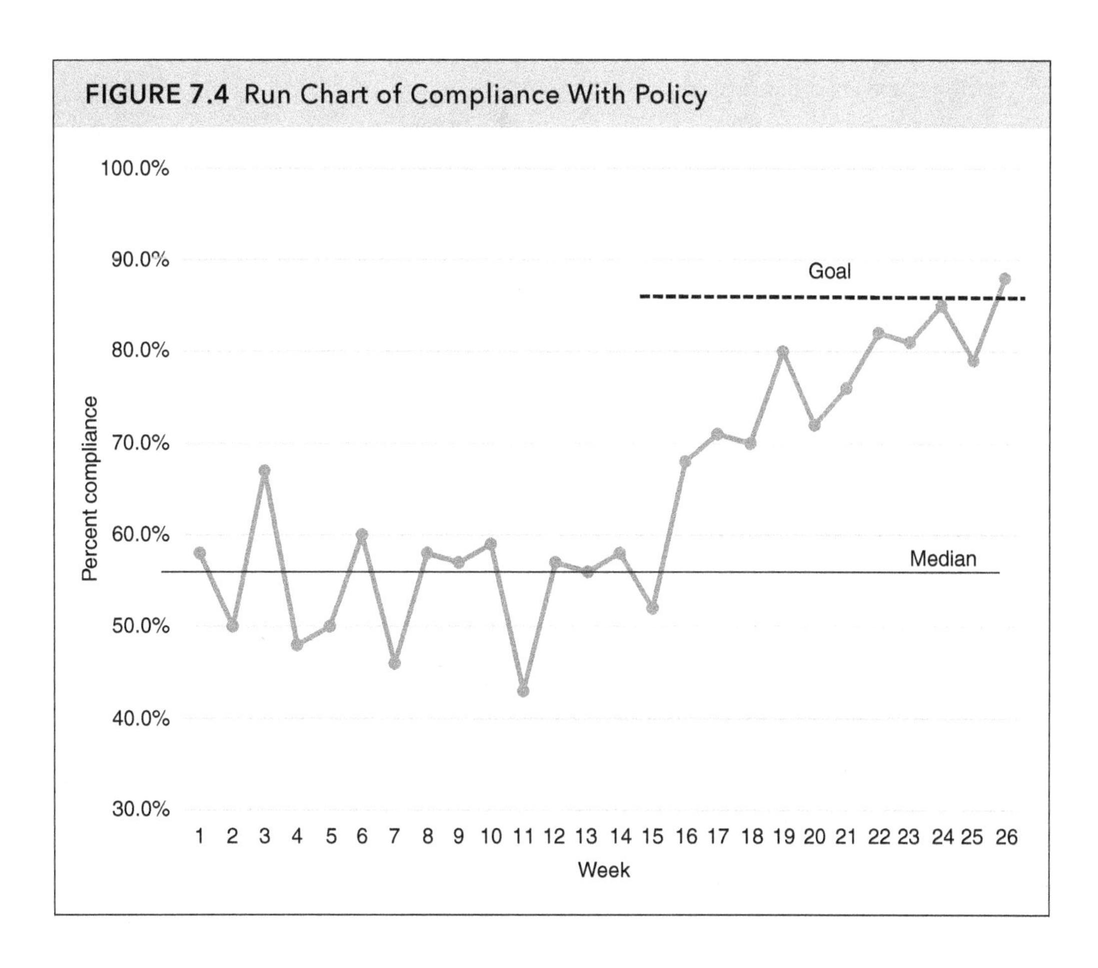

The Balanced Scorecard Model

The **balanced scorecard** is used to communicate what the organization is trying to accomplish, align day-to-day (operational) work with strategy, prioritize projects/services, and measure and monitor progress toward completion of strategies and objectives. The balanced scorecard considers "perspectives" of a healthcare organization—financial/stewardship, customer/stakeholder, internal process, and organizational capacity—to develop **key performance indicators (KPIs)**, measurable values that can be used to assess how well an organization is meeting its objectives.

KEY QUESTIONS TO ASK IN DEVELOPING STRATEGIC AREAS FOR KEY PERFORMANCE INDICATORS

1. What is our main financial goal?
2. What do we want our customers to say about our organization?
3. What processes are critical to our operational success?
4. How can we make employees more effective?

TABLE 7.4 Balanced Scorecard

Balanced Scorecard Perspective	Examples of Strategic Areas
Financial/stewardship	• Financial performance • Effective resource use
Customer/stakeholder	• Customer value • Satisfaction and/or retention
Internal process	• Efficiency • Quality
Organizational capacity	• Human resources • Infrastructure and technology

Examples of strategic areas using this model are shown in Table 7.4.

One way that the balanced scorecard can be used effectively is to visualize and communicate how value is created. In Figure 7.5 we see that improving performance in the strategic area of organizational capacity allows the organization to improve its internal process perspective. Improving performance in strategic areas in internal process allows the organization to improve its customer/stakeholder perspective, and improving performance in strategic areas in customer/stakeholder allows the organization to improve its financial/stewardship perspective.

For each objective developed, at least one KPI should be identified and tracked over time, to provide an assessment of whether a strategy is working. KPIs are used to monitor strategies and to identify gaps between targeted performance and actual performance. Good KPIs allow an organization to determine its level of efficiency and effectiveness, provide an objective way of determining if a strategy is working, allow measurement and gauge performance over time, and focus attention on what is required for success.

Common KPIs that healthcare organizations track, depending on the type of organization and services offered, include:

- Patient wait time
- Average length of stay
- Emergency department (ED) wait times
- Average time to process claims
- Claims denial rate
- Average treatment cost by age
- Hospital readmission rates
- Percentage of population immunized
- Patient satisfaction
- Cost by payer type

FIGURE 7.5 Visualization of the Balanced Scorecard Strategic Area: Organizational Capacity

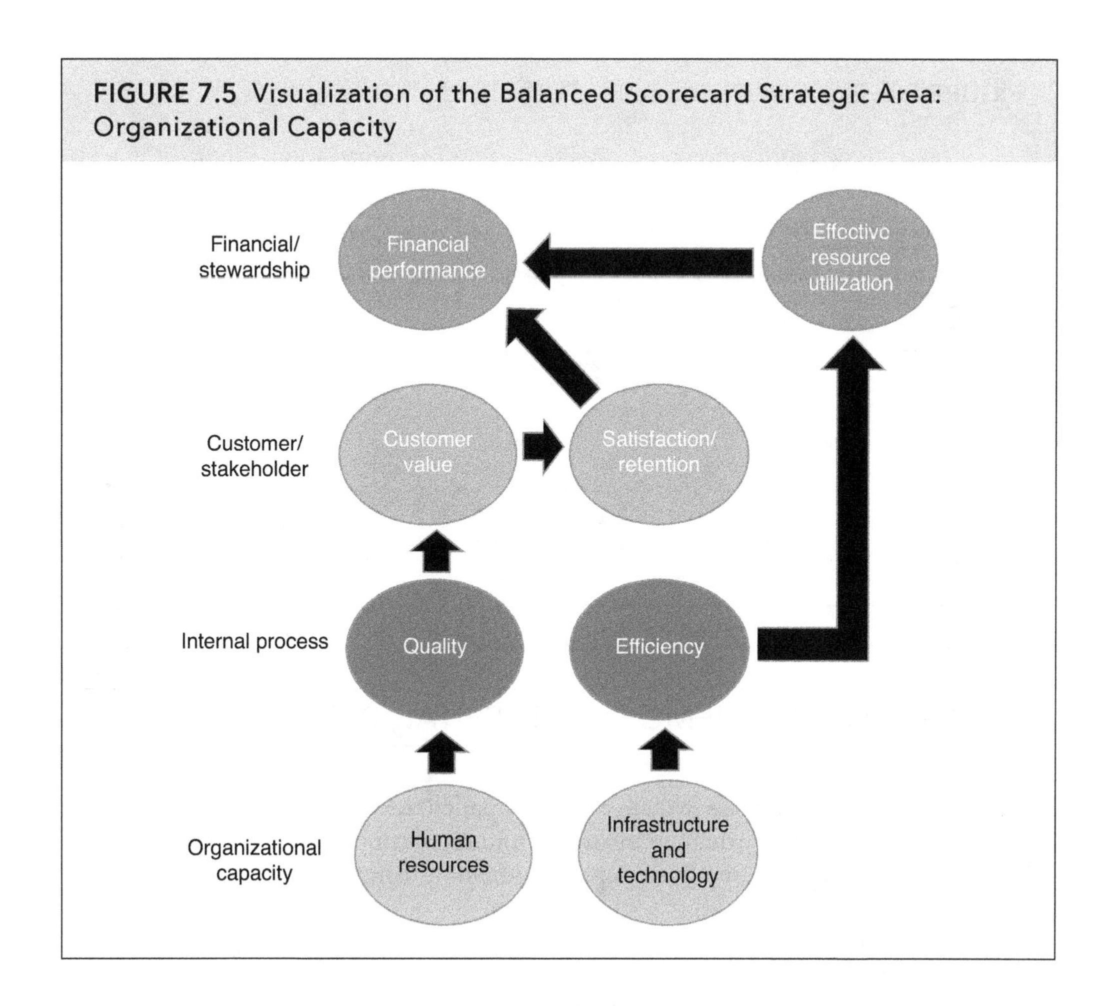

Once a baseline has been established, KPIs can be compared against the baseline. KPIs are commonly presented in graphic format as a **dashboard**, which is a visual assessment methodology that can be used to assess KPIs. Dashboards are based on real-time or near real-time data and can be reviewed quickly. An example of a financial performance dashboard for a community hospital is presented in Figure 7.6.

KPIs can also be compared over time to analyze trends and progression toward improvement. When evaluating against previous year performance, it is best to make comparisons on a month-to-month basis, as season variations can affect performance. It is also important to consider other factors that can impact performance, such as a disease outbreak, employee vacations, changes in policy, and other internal and external events.

FIGURE 7.6 Financial Performance Dashboard

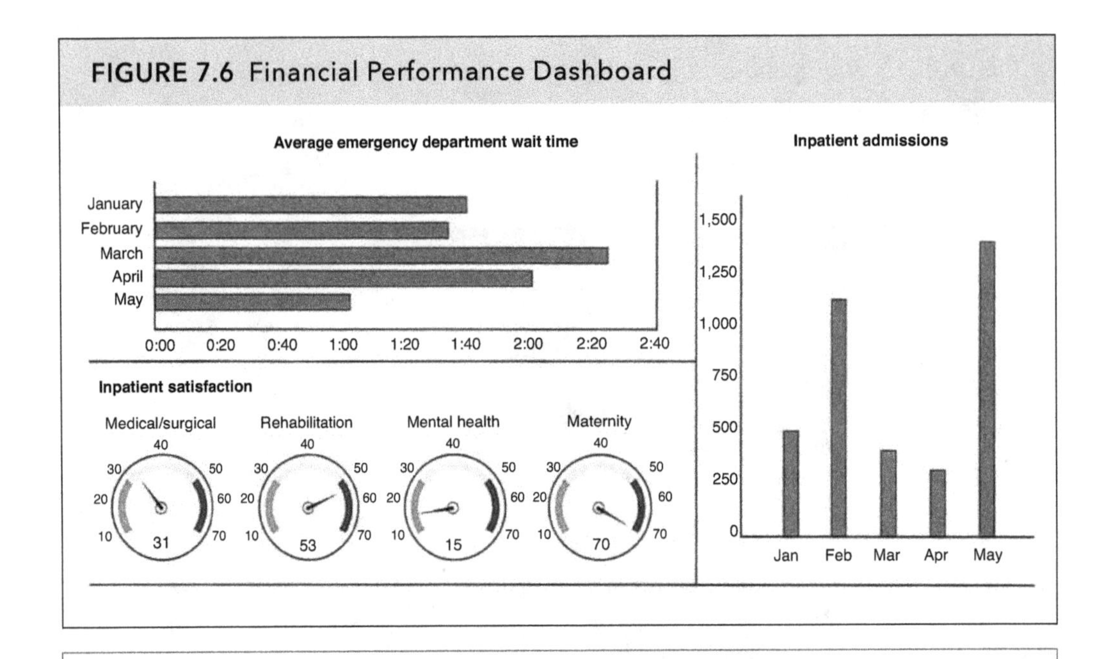

CASE STUDY MEMORIAL HOSPITAL, INC.

Objective 1.1: To increase private insurance patient revenues in the five identified (based on growth of privately insured population) counties by 5% in the next 12 months, by targeting the five counties with advertising and physician-relations campaigns.

The strategic planning committee worked with the director of Planning & Marketing to develop evaluation plans for Strategy 1.1a (see the following table). The marketing plan will include a mix of television, radio, and billboard advertising distributed across the five counties according to population size. It is now December 31, 20X0 and an outside marketing firm is under contract.

Objective 1.1: To increase private insurance patient revenues in the five identified (based on growth of privately insured population) counties by 5% in the next 12 months, by targeting the five counties with advertising and physician-relations campaigns.
Strategy 1.1a: Develop and implement a comprehensive marketing plan targeting the five counties.

Responsibility: Chief Operating Officer	Resource Requirements	Target Completion	Responsibility	Complete? If No, Reason
• Select outside marketing firm and sign contract for marketing campaign	$100,000	December 15, 20X0	Director, Planning & Marketing	Yes

(continued)

CASE STUDY MEMORIAL HOSPITAL, INC. (*continued*)

Responsibility: Chief Operating Officer	Resource Requirements	Target Completion	Responsibility	Complete? If No, Reason
• Approve marketing campaign	$0	January 30, 20X1	Director, Planning & Marketing	
• Implement marketing campaign	$200,000	July 1, 20X1-June 20, 20X2	Director, Planning & Marketing	
• PDSA–marketing campaign by county	$0	October 1, 20X1	Director, Planning & Marketing	
• PDSA–marketing campaign by county	$0	January 1, 20X2	Director, Planning & Marketing	
• PDSA–marketing campaign by county	$0	April 1, 20X2	Director, Planning & Marketing	
• PDSA–marketing campaign by county	$0	July 1, 20X2	Director, Planning & Marketing	
• Evaluate effectiveness of marketing campaign	$0	August 1, 20X2	Director, Planning & Marketing	

(*continued*)

CASE STUDY MEMORIAL HOSPITAL, INC. (*continued*)

The strategic planning committee worked with the director of Physician Relations to develop evaluation plans for Strategy 1.1b (see the following table). Physician Relations will market services to targeted physicians—those with high private patient market share—in the five counties. It is now May 1, 20X1.

Objective 1.1: To increase private insurance patient revenues in the five identified (based on growth of privately insured population) counties by 5% in the next 12 months, by targeting the five counties with advertising and physician-relations campaigns. **Strategy 1.1b: Work with Physician Relations to continue building physician relationships in the five counties and increase referrals.**				
Responsibility: Chief Operating Officer	**Resource Requirements**	**Target Completion**	**Responsibility**	**Complete? If No, Reason**
• Monthly lunch in identified offices	$20,000	July 1, 20X1-June 30, 20X2	Director, Physician Relations	
• Branded materials for offices	$5,000	July 1, 20X1-June 30, 20X2	Director, Physician Relations	

The following evaluation and control worksheet will aid you in developing tools to measure progress toward your healthcare organization's objectives.

EVALUATION AND CONTROL WORKSHEET

Answer the Following Questions

1. What kind of information do you need to evaluate a program's or service's success?

____

____

____

____

2. Who should receive and review this information?

____

3. What time periods do you want to use to analyze the data? Weekly? Monthly?

4. What record-keeping system do you need to develop to make sure the information you want is recorded for the time periods you specified in question 3?

Now Set Up Your Control Procedures

1. Specify the areas to be controlled:

   A. ___

   B. ___

   C. ___

   D. ___

2. Specify the format of the data for each area. (Is it likely to be numbers by month by program? Do you want number and percentage variations?)

   A. ___

   B. ___

   C. ___

   D. ___

3. Specify how the data are to be collected, who is to collect and analyze the data, and who is to receive the results of the analysis:

   A. How will the data be collected?

B. Who has responsibility to collect and analyze the data?

____

____

C. Who is to receive which type of analysis?

Administrator	Types of Analysis
1. ________________	1. ________________
2. ________________	2. ________________
3. ________________	3. ________________
4. ________________	4. ________________

GLOSSARY OF TERMS

Balanced scorecard—tracking methodology used to communicate what the organization is trying to accomplish, align day-to-day (operational) work with strategy, prioritize projects/services, and measure and monitor progress toward completion of strategies and objectives. The balanced scorecard considers "perspectives" of a healthcare organization—financial/stewardship, customer/stakeholder, internal process, and organizational capacity—to develop key performance indicators (KPIs).

Budget—a plan for how resources (commonly money) will be used to support objectives

Dashboard—a visual assessment methodology that can be used to quickly assess KPIs

Evaluation and control of services provided—assessment of budgeted/projected services provided versus actual services provided

Patient/client feedback—reactions from those you serve, which can be used as an evaluation measure

Revenue/cost control—measure of how well the financial health of an organization is being managed

Financial ratios—mathematical formulas used to evaluate financial performance against expectations, historical trends, and the industry

Key performance indicators (KPIs)—a measurable value that can be used to assess how well an organization is meetings its objectives

Pareto chart (Pareto diagram)—a quality improvement tool that is used to identify factors that contribute to a project or process, allowing a team to concentrate on those factors that have the greatest impact

PDSA (plan–do–study–act) cycle—a problem-solving process used for quality improvement initiatives

Run chart—graphs data over time and is used to assess change

CHAPTER 8

SAMPLE STRATEGIC PLANS

We don't like their sound, and guitar music is on the way out.

—Decca Recording Company
Rejecting the Beatles in 1962

In the end, a strong strategic plan helps to protect an organization from threats in a changing environment. It also allows organizations to position themselves to take advantage of opportunities that present themselves due to change. Decca Recording Company was not positioned, for whatever reasons, to see the opportunity to represent the Beatles in the United States—a role that Capitol Records was happy to fill.

This chapter contains two strategic plans: Florida Department of Health Strategic Plan (2017) and Health Resources and Services Administration (n.d.). Consider these questions as you review each plan:

1. How would you evaluate the plan?
2. Can you see how the steps in the planning cycle were used to inform what you read?
3. How well are the objectives written? Are they SMART?
4. Is the plan realistic?
5. Can objectives be measured and/or the plan evaluated?
6. Are there any parts of the plan that are not supported?
7. Does the plan include an evaluation feedback loop?

Keep in mind that these are the final, implemented, publicly available plans. They do not reveal market analysis, options considered, and other important inputs into the planning process that you now know. Also, they may not reveal proprietary information or strategy.

■ ■ ■

HEALTH RESOURCES AND SERVICES ADMINISTRATION

STRATEGIC PLAN FY 2016-FY 2018

INTRODUCTION

The Health Resources and Services Administration (HRSA), an Agency of the U.S. Department of Health and Human Services, is the primary federal agency for improving access to health care for the tens of millions of Americans who, for a variety of reasons, are medically underserved or face barriers to needed care. This *Strategic Plan FY 2016-FY 2018* is a blueprint for HRSA as it addresses ongoing access and service delivery issues in the context of an evolving healthcare system. The Plan reflects the Agency's commitment to build upon past successes while advancing its mission to improve health and achieve health equity through access to quality services, a skilled health workforce and innovative programs. The Strategic Plan sets forth five mission-critical goals:

Goal 1: Improve Access to Quality Health Care and Services
Goal 2: Strengthen the Health Workforce
Goal 3: Build Healthy Communities
Goal 4: Improve Health Equity
Goal 5: Strengthen HRSA Program Management and Operations

Because of their continuing relevance the first four goals are the same as those in HRSA's *Strategic Plan 2010-2015*. A fifth goal has been added to focus on improving and strengthening operational and programmatic efficiency and effectiveness.

For each of these goals, objectives and strategies are outlined. Given the broad range and complexity of HRSA's programs, the Plan is not an inventory of all objectives HRSA will pursue or all actions that it will undertake. Instead, the Plan presents *priority* objectives reflecting important changes and outcomes that HRSA hopes to achieve, and *key* strategies that indicate the main approaches the Agency intends to take to meet these objectives. The Plan also identifies *key* performance measures that will be used to track and evaluate progress toward meeting the Agency's goals.

The Strategic Plan will help inform program- and operational-level planning and resource allocation decisions over the next three years. It aligns with the Department of Health and Human Services' *Strategic Plan 2014-2018*. The HRSA plan is a dynamic document to which changes may be made as HRSA adjusts to new circumstances, while keeping its focus on meeting the needs of the communities and individuals it serves and ensuring effective use of taxpayer dollars.

HRSA VISION
Healthy Communities, Healthy People

MISSION
To improve health and achieve health equity through access to quality services, a skilled health workforce and innovative programs

GOALS
Improve Access to Quality Health Care and Services

Strengthen the Health Workforce

Build Healthy Communities

Improve Health Equity

Strengthen HRSA Program Management and Operations

OBJECTIVES AND STRATEGIES

Goal 1: Improve Access to Quality Health Care and Services

Objective 1.1: Increase the capacity and strength of the healthcare safety net.

How We Will Accomplish Our Objective:

- Support an increase in the number of healthcare access points to expand the availability of services to underserved, disadvantaged, geographically isolated, and special needs populations.
- Facilitate and support the recruitment, placement, and retention of primary care and other providers in underserved communities (including through telehealth) in order to address shortages and improve access to care.
- Provide technical assistance to safety-net organizations in order to ensure their financial and operational health and sustainability.
- Strengthen healthcare and related systems and networks through funding, policy development, and other levers to build and support an effective service delivery infrastructure.

Objective 1.2: Improve the quality and efficacy of the healthcare safety net.

How We Will Accomplish Our Objective:

- Provide technical assistance and other supports to providers and care systems to ensure that persons served by HRSA programs receive quality care across their life-span through comprehensive, integrated, and patient-/family-centered medical/health homes.
- Provide performance-based awards to grantees that demonstrate improved patient outcomes as reflected by their clinical quality measures, and assist safety-net providers in quality measurement and reporting.
- Promote efforts of HRSA-funded healthcare providers to achieve Meaningful Use Standards in order to further the optimal use of health information technology.
- Work with safety-net providers, networks, and systems to promote their assessment of and potential participation in value-based healthcare payment systems.
- Establish and evaluate formal learning and action collaboratives among HRSA grantees and other stakeholders in order to advance learning, enhance quality of care, and achieve system-wide improvements.

Objective 1.3: Increase enrollment in and utilization of health insurance through Medicaid, CHIP, and the Health Insurance Marketplace.

How We Will Accomplish Our Objective:

- Provide funding, technical assistance, and other resources for health coverage outreach, education, and enrollment activities of HRSA grantees and other stakeholders.
- Disseminate culturally and linguistically appropriate information and educate HRSA grantees and other stakeholders in order to aid them in helping underserved populations better understand how to utilize healthcare coverage, understand benefits, and connect to primary care and preventive services.
- Document and share lessons learned from outreach, education, and enrollment activities.

Goal 2: Strengthen the Health Workforce

Objective 2.1: Advance the competencies of the healthcare and public health workforce.

How We Will Accomplish Our Objective:

- Support curriculum development and the training of health professionals to ensure the learning, enhancement, and updating of essential knowledge and skills.
- Support training and other activities that enhance the health workforce's competency in providing culturally and linguistically appropriate care.
- Expand the number and type of training and technical assistance opportunities that educate students and providers to work in interprofessional teams and participate in practice transformations.
- Support technical assistance, training, and other opportunities to help safety-net providers expand, coordinate, and effectively use health information technology to support service delivery and quality improvement.
- Provide information and technical assistance to ensure that HRSA-supported safety-net providers know and use current treatment guidelines, appropriate promising practices, and evidence-based models of care.

Objective 2.2: Increase the diversity and distribution of the health workforce and the ability of providers to serve underserved populations and areas.

How We Will Accomplish Our Objective:

- Facilitate and support the recruitment, placement, and retention of primary care and other providers in underserved communities in order to address shortages and improve the distribution of the health workforce.
- Support outreach and other activities to increase the recruitment, training, placement, and retention of under-represented groups in the health workforce.
- Support pre-entry academic advising, mentoring, and enrichment activities for underrepresented groups in order to promote successful health professions training and career development.
- Promote training opportunities within community-based settings for health professions students and residents by enhancing partnerships with organizations serving the underserved.

Objective 2.3: Enhance focus on health workforce assessment and policy analysis.

How We Will Accomplish Our Objective:

- Develop and employ approaches to monitoring, forecasting, and meeting long-term health workforce needs.
- Provide policy makers, researchers, and the public with information on health workforce trends, supply, demand, and policy issues.

Goal 3: Build Healthy Communities

Objective 3.1: Improve population health through the use of community partnerships and collaboration with stakeholders.

How We Will Accomplish Our Objective:

- Develop and support partnerships with stakeholders in the health and non-health sectors in order to link people to services and resources that improve population health.
- Engage with communities and stakeholders to develop, plan, and coordinate public health initiatives that span the prevention and care continuum.
- Support the integration and coordination of public health with primary care, including behavioral and oral health services, to improve individual outcomes and overall population health.

Objective 3.2: Strengthen the focus on health promotion and disease prevention across populations, providers, and communities.

How We Will Accomplish Our Objective:

- Inform and educate vulnerable populations about health promotion, disease prevention, and health behaviors that improve individual and population health, and about HRSA's programs that contribute to population health improvement.
- Strengthen safety-net providers' attention to the provision of health promotion and disease prevention services, and include prevention and health promotion practices as regular elements of HRSA-supported programs.
- Support improvements in health-related infrastructure systems that contribute to population health.

Objective 3.3: Increase understanding of what works in health care and public health practice to address community needs.

How We Will Accomplish Our Objective:

- Promote and use community health needs assessments, environmental surveillance, and other tools in order to more effectively target and distribute resources, and inform program improvements.
- Support demonstrations and innovative practices to test and refine approaches to improving population health.
- Collect and analyze patient and population data to track progress in achieving Healthy People 2020 and other national objectives.

Goal 4: Improve Health Equity

Objective 4.1: Reduce disparities in access and quality of care, and improve health outcomes across populations and communities.

How We Will Accomplish Our Objective:

- Target investments and technical assistance toward communities and organizations that address the needs of vulnerable populations, and promote quality improvement activities that advance health equity.
- Focus resources and services on diseases and conditions with the greatest health disparities and promote outreach efforts to reach populations most affected.
- Integrate cultural competency into HRSA programs, policies, and practices to ensure the delivery of culturally and linguistically appropriate care.
- Conduct targeted outreach and provide technical assistance to entities in underserved communities that have not sought or have been unsuccessful in obtaining HRSA funding.

Objective 4.2: Advance evidence-based, evidence-informed, and innovative practices that have the potential to reduce health disparities.

How We Will Accomplish Our Objective:

- Provide information, technical assistance, and tools to HRSA grantees and other stakeholders on reducing health disparities.
- Develop and strengthen partnerships with entities across different sectors to address the social determinants of health through the integration of public health and primary care.
- Work with diverse communities to create, develop, disseminate, and evaluate innovative solutions to improve health equity.

Objective 4.3: Inform program improvement efforts by assessing the effectiveness of HRSA programs in addressing health disparities.

How We Will Accomplish Our Objective:

- Increase efforts that advance data collection and data analysis capacity to examine differences in access/quality/outcomes by sub-groups served by HRSA.
- Develop performance measures to track disparity patterns among populations served by HRSA and use the information for program improvement.
- Support and collaborate in research and demonstration efforts that advance the understanding of health disparities in order to inform HRSA initiatives.

Goal 5: Strengthen HRSA Program Management and Operations

Objective 5.1: Improve efficiency and effectiveness of operations.

How We Will Accomplish Our Objective:

- Support the development, enhancement, and use of technology at the enterprise level to assist the HRSA workforce in performing at the highest levels.
- Integrate financial, programmatic, and customer data to support decision-making that drives operational and business process improvements.
- Empower the HRSA workforce to design, test, and sustain innovative approaches to improving operational and business processes.
- Support a mobile work environment that balances flexibility with accountability and high-level performance.

Objective 5.2: Strengthen the HRSA workforce to support a performance-driven organization.

How We Will Accomplish Our Objective

- Recruit, hire, and retain a talented and diverse HRSA workforce based on the needs of the organization and in alignment with workforce planning principles.
- Conduct training and expand other opportunities for team and individual competency development to support a skilled workforce at all levels of the organization.
- Hold the HRSA workforce accountable by implementing meaningful and timely appraisal processes, and recognize employee contributions toward achieving HRSA goals.

Objective 5.3: Enhance program oversight and integrity.

How We Will Accomplish Our Objective:

- Foster collaboration among HRSA staff to improve communication that strengthens program oversight and integrity.
- Integrate risk management techniques as an integral part of program oversight to drive strategic decision-making.
- Identify internal and external risks to program performance, and monitor programs, contractors and award recipients to proactively address and prevent program vulnerabilities.

Objective 5.4: Promote a customer-centered culture.

***How We Will Accomplish Our Objective*:**

- Promote timeliness by improving processes to respond to internal and external requests for information or assistance.
- Work with the HRSA workforce and stakeholders to develop, test, implement, and sustain innovative customer-centered principles, standards, and practices.
- Expand the use of technology and other electronic tools to enhance communication internally and with stakeholders and the public.

OVERVIEW OF HRSA'S PRINCIPAL PROGRAMS

HRSA has an annual budget of approximately $10 billion, operates over 80 different programs, and awards more the 10,000 grants and supplements to approximately 3,000 partner organizations. Comprising five bureaus and ten offices, HRSA provides leadership and financial support to health care providers, health professions schools, local health systems, states, and other entities throughout the U.S. and its territories.

Health Center Program - Funds nearly 1,300 grantees to provide dependable, high-quality primary and preventive care at over 9,000 clinical sites that serve nearly 23 million patients regardless of their ability to pay, forming a major part of the nation's healthcare safety net.

Ryan White HIV/AIDS Program - Supports 900 grantees in providing top-quality health care to more than half a million people living with HIV, representing nearly 60 percent of persons with HIV infection in the United States. The Program also supports access to life-saving drug treatment regimens for low-income, underinsured, and uninsured people with HIV.

National Health Service Corps - Provides scholarships and loan repayments to encourage primary care and other clinical care providers to serve in health professional shortage areas, addressing the scarcity of health professionals in needy communities.

Health Workforce Training Programs - Give financial support to educational institutions and healthcare delivery sites for training and curriculum development, and for scholarship and loan repayment for health professions students and faculty to support a diverse workforce that is technically skilled, culturally appropriate, and suited for a contemporary practice environment that includes interprofessional team-based care.

Maternal and Child Health Block Grant Program - Provides grants to 59 states and U.S. jurisdictions to support health systems infrastructure development, public information and education, screening and counseling, and other services (including direct care services as payer of last resort) that annually reach more than 41 million women, infants, children, and children with special health care needs.

Rural Health Policy Program - Advises the Department of Health and Human Services on health policy issues impacting health care finance, workforce, and access to care in rural areas. Also runs state- and community-based grant, technical assistance, and telehealth programs that work to build capacity in rural communities and help meet the health needs of rural residents; and supports research on issues related to the delivery and financing of health care in rural America.

Other HRSA Programs - HRSA oversees or supports many other activities that are critical to the nation's health and well-being, including: the Healthy Start Program; the national network of poison control centers; national organ procurement and allocation activities; the National Vaccine Injury and Countermeasures Injury Compensation Programs; the 340B Drug Pricing Program; the Maternal, Infant, and Early Childhood Home Visiting Program; Hansen's Disease treatment, training, and research programs; and the National Practitioner Data Bank that helps improve healthcare quality, protect the public, and reduce healthcare fraud and abuse. HRSA is also responsible for the federal designation of Health Professional Shortage Areas and Medically Underserved Areas/Populations.

PERFORMANCE MEASURES

Achieving high performance in pursuing its mission is a major priority for HRSA. The measures presented below have been selected, from among the many measures used by HRSA to review performance, as points of focus for tracking and evaluating the status and progress in addressing Strategic Plan goals.

Goal 1: Improve Access to Quality Health Care and Services

Access

- Number of patients served by health centers
- Percent of eligible persons diagnosed with HIV served by the Ryan White HIV/AIDS Program
- Number of unique individuals receiving direct services through the Federal Office of Rural Health Policy Outreach grants
- Number of participants served by the Maternal, Infant, and Early Childhood Home Visiting Program

Quality

- Percent of patients served by the Ryan White Program, regardless of age, with a HIV viral load less than 200copies/mL at last HIV viral load test during the measurement year
- Percent of health centers meeting or exceeding Healthy People 2020 goals on selected quality measures
- Percent of Home Visiting participants who received appropriate screening for: (a) depression, (b) interpersonal violence, (c) developmental delay

Outreach and Enrollment

- Number of assists provided by trained assisters working on behalf of health centers to support individuals with actual or potential enrollment/reenrollment in health insurance available through Marketplace-qualified health plans and/or through Medicaid or CHIP

Goal 2: Strengthen the Health Workforce

- Field strength of the National Health Service Corps through scholarship and loan repayment agreements
- Percentage of individuals supported by the Bureau of Health Workforce who completed a primary care training program and are currently employed in underserved areas
- Percentage of trainees in Bureau of Health Workforce-supported health professions training programs who receive training in medically underserved communities
- Percentage of trainees in Bureau of Health Workforce programs who are underrepresented minorities and/or from disadvantaged backgrounds

Goal 3: Build Healthy Communities

- Number of pregnant women and children served by the Maternal and Child Health Block Grant
- Percent of low birth weight births among Healthy Start program participants
- Percent of health centers providing: (a) oral health, (b) behavioral health, and (c) specific preventive health services
- Percent of donated kidneys used for transplantation

Goal 4: Improve Health Equity

- Percent of (a) health centers and (b) Ryan White programs that have reduced disparities on specific clinical performance measures
- Number of blood stem cell transplants facilitated for minority patients by the C.W. Bill Young Cell Transplantation Program

Goal 5: Strengthen HRSA Program Management and Operations

- Percent of HRSA products and services (e.g., FOAs, correspondence, reports, audits, technical assistance) that meet established quality and timeliness benchmarks
- Program customer satisfaction: Percent of HRSA awardees reporting positively on key indicators
- Employee satisfaction: Percent of HRSA staff reporting positively on key indicators

Florida Department of Health

Agency Strategic Plan 2016–2018

Rick Scott

GOVERNOR

John H. Armstrong, MD, FACS

STATE SURGEON GENERAL
AND SECRETARY

Version 1.5

Published January 2016

Produced by:

Florida Department of Health
4052 Bald Cypress Way, Bin # A00
Tallahassee, FL 32399-1701

TABLE OF CONTENTS

EXECUTIVE SUMMARY

The Florida Department of Health conducted a strategic planning process during the summer of 2015 to define the direction and course of the agency for consumers, employees, administrators and legislators for the next three years. This strategic plan will position the Department to operate as a sustainable integrated public health system under the current economic environment and to provide our residents and visitors with high quality public health services. This is a living document that we will evaluate and update regularly to address new challenges posed by the changing environment of public health in Florida.

Executive leadership championed the planning process which involved participation from numerous internal stakeholders including division and office directors, county health officers, program managers and program staff over a two month period. Leadership also engaged in discussions with staff from the Executive Office of the Governor, the Department's governing body, during the planning process. We considered key support functions required for efficiency and effectiveness and sought to articulate what we plan to achieve as an organization, the actions we will take, and how we will measure our success.

The Department approached the strategic planning process with a number of guiding principles in mind:

- Children, adults, and families are at the center of public health activities.
- Individuals, families, businesses, schools, civic organizations, faith-based groups and local government are responsible for child, adult, family and community health.
- Social determinants dominate health outcomes.
- Health equity promotion is part of every public health activity.
- Interventions to promote public health are evidence-based and community supported.
- Veterans deserve particular support.

Mission – Why do we exist?
To protect, promote and improve the health of all people in Florida through integrated state, county and community efforts.

Vision – What do we want to achieve?
To be the Healthiest State in the Nation.

Values – What do we use to achieve our mission and vision?
I nnovation: We search for creative solutions and manage resources wisely.
C ollaboration: We use teamwork to achieve common goals & solve problems.
A ccountability: We perform with integrity & respect.
R esponsiveness: We achieve our mission by serving our customers & engaging our partners.
E xcellence: We promote quality outcomes through learning & continuous performance improvement.

STRATEGY MAP

STRATEGIC PRIORITY AREAS	STRATEGIES	OBJECTIVES
HEALTHY MOMS AND BABIES **GOAL:** Eliminate infant mortality	• Eliminate racial disparity in infant mortality	• Reduce the three-year rolling average of black infant mortality rate from 10.9 (2012-2014) to 8.3 per 1,000 live births and reduce black-white infant mortality gap from 2.25 to less than 2 times higher or reduce the black-white infant mortality gap by 12%.
LONG, HEALTHY LIFE **GOAL:** Increase healthy life expectancy	• Increase the healthy weight of children and adults • Improve the cardiovascular health of adults • Reduce cancer incidence and increase cancer survival • Reduce injury • Reduce HIV incidence • Reduce the incidence of Alzheimer's disease and related dementias	• Increase the percentage of children in grade 1 who are at a healthy weight from 66% (2013) to 70%. • Increase the percentage of adults in Florida who are at a healthy weight from 35% (2013) to 38%. • Reduce the number of adults who report ever being told they had coronary heart disease, heart attack, or stroke from 10.3% (2013) to 9.8%. • Reduce the rate of new cancer from 424.6 (2012) to 400 per 100,000. • Decrease the unintentional injury crude death rate from 46.7 (2014) to 38.7 per 100,000. • Reduce the annual number of newly diagnosed HIV infections in Florida from 4,613 (2014) to 4,255. • Reduce the annual number of newly diagnosed HIV infections in Florida's black population from 2,024 (2014) to 1,867. • Increase the proportion of ADAP clients with an undetectable viral load from 89% (2014) to 92%. • Reduce the rate per 100,000 of total early syphilis in Florida from 18.5 (2014) to 17.9. • Establish five partnerships for developing activities that can impact the incidence of Alzheimer's disease and related dementias.
READINESS FOR EMERGING HEALTH THREATS **GOAL:** Demonstrate readiness for emerging health threats	• Increase vaccination rates for children and adults • Improve Florida ESSENCE systems to better provide just-in-time data on syndromic events • Improve Florida's National Health Security Preparedness Index (NHSPI) • Decrease inhaled nicotine use among children and adults	• Increase the percent of 2 year olds who are fully immunized from 86% (2014) to 90%. • Increase percent of teens who have completed the first HPV shot from 57.2% (2014) to 70%. • Convert all 88 facilities using flat files to HL7 for ESSENCE. • Increase the number of hospitals participating in electronic lab reporting (ELR) from 52 (2014) to 110. • Increase Florida's National Health Security Preparedness Index (NHSPI) score from 7.8 (2014) to 8.1. • Decrease current inhaled nicotine prevalence in youth age 11-17 from 14.7% (2014) to 12.6%. • Decrease current inhaled nicotine prevalence in adults from 21.3% (2014) to 19.2%.
EFFECTIVE AGENCY PROCESSES **GOAL:** Establish a sustainable infrastructure, which includes a competent workforce, standardized business practices and effective use of technology.	• Increase the number of communications products (e.g. press releases, infographics, social media) • Increase the percentage of employees with complete Individual Development Plan (vs. completion of Learning Management System activities) • Ensure balanced operational budgets • Implement an actuarially sound administrative component of the Children's Medical Services managed care plan. • Publish public health best practices in nationally recognized journals	• Increase communication products from 3000 (2015) to 3600. • Increase participation of DOH employees in one or more professional development opportunities to 50%. • 100% of programs are functioning within their annual operating budgets • Complete a comparative analysis of agency IT expenditure. • Implement the operational plan for Human Resources Consortiums. • Provide evidence for value/ROI for consolidating billing functions. • Reduce administrative costs associated with Title XIX and Title XXI to 6.5-8.0% of plan expenditures. • Publish 5 articles regarding the Department's accomplishments in peer-reviewed journals.
REGULATORY EFFICIENCY **GOAL:** Establish a regulatory structure that supports the state's strategic priorities related to global competitiveness and economic growth	• Reduce lines of regulation • Increase percentage of licensed health professionals • Standardize department regulatory systems • Increase efficiency in disability claims processing	• Reduce the number of lines of regulation by 15% from 71,442 (2015) to 60,725. • Reduce by 50% the percentage of deficient applications received from 74% (2015) to 37%. • Increase the number of applications approved for health care licensure of military spouses and honorably discharged veterans by 50% from 137 (2015) to 206. • Establish enterprise solutions for all department regulatory functions. • Ensure that 3 of 4 quarterly (FL disability) claim processing times are less than the national average processing time.

STRATEGIC PRIORITIES

Priority 1: Healthy Moms and Babies
Goal 1.1: Eliminate infant mortality

Strategy	Objective	
1.1.1 Eliminate racial disparity in infant mortality	A	By December 31, 2018, reduce the three-year rolling average of black infant mortality rate from 10.9 (2012-2014) to 8.3 per 1,000 live births and reduce black-white infant mortality gap from 2.25 to less than 2 times higher or reduce the black-white infant mortality gap by 12%.

Priority 2: Long, Healthy Life
Goal 2.1: Increase healthy life expectancy

Strategy	Objective	
2.1.1 Increase the healthy weight of children and adults	A	By December 31, 2018, increase the percentage of children in grade 1 who are at a healthy weight from 66% (2013) to 70%.
	B	By December 31, 2018, increase the percentage of adults in Florida who are at a healthy weight from 35% (2013) to 38%.
2.1.2 Improve the cardiovascular health of adults	A	By December 31, 2018, reduce the number of adults who report ever being told they had coronary heart disease, heart attack, or stroke from 10.3% (2013) to 9.8%.
2.1.3 Reduce cancer incidence and increase cancer survival	A	By December 31, 2018, reduce the rate of new cancer from 424.6 (2012) to 400 per 100,000.
2.1.4 Reduce injury	A	By December 31, 2018, decrease the unintentional injury crude death rate from 46.7 (2014) to 38.7 per 100,000.
2.1.5 Reduce HIV incidence	A	By December 31, 2018, reduce the annual number of newly diagnosed HIV infections in Florida from 4,613 (2014) to 4,255.
	B	By December 31, 2018, reduce the annual number of newly diagnosed HIV infections in Florida's black population from 2,024 (2014) to 1,867.
	C	By December 31, 2018, increase the proportion of ADAP clients with an undetectable viral load from 89% (2014) to 92%.
	D	By December 31, 2018, reduce the rate per 100,000 of total early syphilis in Florida from 18.5 (2014) to 17.9.
2.1.6 Reduce the incidence of Alzheimer's disease and related dementias	A	By December 31, 2018, establish five partnerships for developing activities that can impact the incidence of Alzheimer's disease and related dementias.

Priority 3: Readiness for Emerging Health Threats
Goal 3.1: Demonstrate readiness for emerging health threats

Strategy		Objective
3.1.1 Increase vaccination rates for children and adults	A	By December 31, 2018, increase the percent of 2 year olds who are fully immunized from 86% (2014) to 90%.
	B	By December 31, 2018, increase percent of teens who have completed the first HPV shot from 57.2% (2014) to 70%.
3.1.2 Improve Florida ESSENCE systems to better provide just-in-time data on syndromic events	A	By December 31, 2018, all 88 facilities using flat files to populate ESSENCE will convert to HL7.
	B	By December 31, 2018, increase the number of hospitals participating in electronic lab reporting (ELR) from 52 (2014) to 110.
3.1.3 Improve Florida's National Health Security Preparedness Index	A	By December 31, 2018, increase Florida's National Health Security Preparedness Index (NHSPI) score from 7.8 (2014) to 8.1.
3.1.4 Decrease inhaled nicotine use among children and adults	A	By December 31, 2018, decrease current inhaled nicotine* prevalence in Florida youth age 11-17 from 14.7% (2014) to 12.6%. *Inhaled nicotine includes cigarettes, cigars, flavored cigarettes, flavored cigars, hookah, and e-cigarettes.
	B	By December 31, 2018, decrease current inhaled nicotine** prevalence in adults from 21.3% (2014) to 19.2%. **Adult inhaled nicotine includes cigarettes, cigars, hookah, and e-cigarettes.

Priority 4: Effective Agency Processes
Goal 4.1: Establish a sustainable infrastructure, which includes a competent workforce, standardized business practices and effective use of technology.

Strategy		Objective
4.1.1 Increase the number of communications products (e.g. press releases, infographics, social media)	A	By June 30, 2018, increase communication products from 3000 (2015) to 3600.
4.1.2 Increase the percentage of employees with complete Individual Development Plan (vs. completion of Learning Management System activities)	A	By December 31, 2018, increase participation of DOH employees in one or more professional development opportunities to 50%.
4.1.3 Ensure balanced operational budgets	A	By June 30, 2016, 100% of programs are functioning within their annual operating budgets
	B	By December 31, 2016, complete a comparative analysis of agency IT expenditure.
	C	By December 31, 2016, implement the operational plan for Human Resources Consortiums.
	D	By December 31, 2016, provide evidence for value/ROI for consolidating billing functions.

Strategy		Objective
4.1.4 Implement an actuarially sound administrative component of the Children's Medical Services managed care plan	A	By December 31, 2017, reduce administrative costs associated with Title XIX and Title XXI to 6.5-8.0% of plan expenditures.
4.1.5 Publish public health best practices in nationally recognized journals	A	By December 31, 2018, publish 5 articles regarding the Department's accomplishments in peer-reviewed journals.

Strategic Priority 5: Regulatory Efficiency
Goal 5: Establish a regulatory structure that supports the state's strategic priorities related to global competitiveness and economic growth.

Strategy		Objective
5.1.1 Reduce lines of regulation	A	By June 30, 2016, reduce the number of lines of regulation by 15% from 71,442 (2015) to 60,725.
5.1.2 Increase percentage of licensed health professionals	A	By December 31, 2017, reduce by 50% the percentage of deficient applications received from 74% (2015) to 37%.
	B	By December 31, 2016, increase the number of applications approved for health care licensure of military spouses and honorably discharged veterans by 50% from 137 (2015) to 206.
5.1.3 Standardize department regulatory systems	A	By December 31, 2017, establish enterprise solutions for all department regulatory functions.
5.1.4 Increase efficiency in disability claims processing	A	By December 31, 2016, ensure that 3 of 4 quarterly (FL disability) claim processing times are less than the national average processing time.

APPENDIX A

The Florida Department of Health Agency Strategic Planning Participants

Executive Leadership

John H. Armstrong, MD, FACS
Surgeon General & Secretary

Kim E. Barnhill, MS, MPH
Deputy Secretary for County Health Systems

Celeste Philip, MD, MPH
Deputy Secretary for Health
Deputy State Health Officer for CMS

J. Martin Stubblefield
Deputy Secretary for Administration

Jennifer A. Tschetter
Chief of Staff

State Health Office Directors

Paul Coley
Office of Performance and Quality Improvement

Tiffany Cowie
Office of Communications

Cindy E. Dick, MBA, EFO
Division of Emergency Preparedness and Community Support

Lucy C. Gee, MS
Division of Medical Quality Assurance

Shannon Hughes
Division of Community Health Promotion

Anna Marie Likos, MD, MPH
Division of Disease Control and Health Protection

Mike Mason
Office of Minority Health

Ed McEachron
Division of Administration

Cassandra G. Pasley, BSN, JD
Division of Children's Medical Services

Tony K. Powell
Office of Information Technology

Patricia L. Ryder, MD, MPH
Division of Public Health Statistics and Performance Management

Michele Tallent
Office of Budget & Revenue Management

Rhonda Wilson
Division of Disability Determinations

County Health Officers

Dawn Allicock, MD, MPH, CPH
DOH—St. Johns

Karen Chapman, MD, MPH
DOH—Okaloosa

Lillian Rivera, PhD, MSN, RN
DOH—Miami-Dade

Mary K Burns, MBA, BSN, RN
DOH—DeSoto

Marsha Player Lindeman, ARNP, MSN
DOH—Gulf

Mike Napier, MS
DOH—Pasco

Claudia Blackburn, MPH, RN
DOH—Leon

Kevin Sherin, MD, MPH, MBA
DOH—Orange

Mark Lander, MS
DOH—Columbia

Program Staff

Deanna Barath, MPH
Statewide Health Programs Administrator

Kathryn Baughman, MPH
Perf. Improvement Consultant

Shay Chapman, BSN, MBA
Chronic Disease Bureau Chief

Cheryl Clark, DrPH
Sr. MCH Epidemiologist

Adrian Cooksey, DrPH, MPH
STD Section Administrator

Felisha Dickey, MPA, MSW
Cancer Program Director

Julia Fitz, MPH
Health Services Program Analyst

Bonnie Gaughan-Bailey, ASQ-CQIA
Division Strategic Ops. Manager

Bob Griffin
Immunization Section Administrator

Tracie Hardin, JD, MSN, BSN, RN Family Planning Program Administrator

Janicka Harris, MPH
Performance Measure Manager

Daphne Holden, PhD
Community Health Improvement Manager

Becky Keyes, ASQ-CMQOE
Planning Consultant

Mike McHargue
Preparedness and Response Bureau Chief

Beth A. Paterniti
Statewide Services Administrator

Sophee Payne
Community Health Assessment Intern

Andy Reich, MS, MSPH, RRT
Interim Environmental Health Bureau Chief

Carol Scoggins, MS
Maternal & Child Health Section Administrator

Phil Street, MPA
Research Manager

Laura Reeves, ASQ, CMQ/OE
TB Section Administrator

APPENDIX B

Planning Summary

The Florida Department of Health executive leadership, composed of the State Surgeon General, the Chief of Staff and the deputies, oversaw the development of the Agency Strategic Plan. Executive leadership first laid out the timeline and framework for the plan, then discussed and agreed to preserve the current mission, vision, and values of the Department. Staff conducted an environmental scan of the agency (sources listed in Appendix E) and executive leadership reviewed the environmental scan and the progress of the current Agency Strategic Plan to formulate potential strategic priority areas. After some deliberation and discussion with the governing body and external partners, they finalized the strategic priority areas: healthy moms and babies; long, healthy life; readiness for emerging health threats; effective agency processes; and regulatory efficiency.

Department staff presented the environmental scan analysis to state health office division and office directors who reviewed the findings and participated in a facilitated discussion of agency strengths, weaknesses, opportunities and threats (SWOT). They included information management, communications, programs and services, budget (financial sustainability), and workforce development as agenda items for discussion in their SWOT meeting. Executive leadership then used the SWOT analysis (Appendix C), environmental scan, agency mission, vision and values to develop agency goals and strategies.

During a two-day, face-to-face meeting with staff from various levels in the Department, including representatives from each regional county health department consortium and program council, input and feedback were provided on the developed goals and strategies, and measurable objectives were developed. Facilitators then worked with program managers and their staff to review and verify the strategies and objectives for each priority area. The revised proposal was then routed back to executive leadership for comment and approval.

The following is the Agency Strategic Plan schedule of meetings:

DATE	MEETING TOPIC	ATTENDEES
June 22, 2015	Establish timeline, mission, vision, and values	Executive Leadership
June 29, 2015	Review environmental scan and discuss possible strategic priority areas	Executive Leadership
July 23, 2015	Finalize strategic priority areas	Executive Leadership, Governing Body & External Partners
July 29, 2015	SWOT Analysis	Executive Leadership & State Health Office Directors
July 30, 2015	Review SWOT analysis and develop goals and strategies for Agency Strategic Plan	Executive Leadership
Aug. 3-4, 2015 (face-to-face meeting)	Review current Agency Strategic Plan, provide input on the goals and propose measurable objectives and activities	Various staff (see appendix A)

DATE	MEETING TOPIC	ATTENDEES
Aug. 11, 2015	Discuss proposal and draft Agency Strategic Plan	Executive Leadership
Aug. 31, 2015	Discuss and modify draft Agency Strategic Plan	Executive Leadership
Sept. 21, 2015	Review final draft of Agency Strategic Plan goals and objectives	Executive Leadership

Monitoring Summary

As depicted in the image below, the strategic planning is a key component of the larger performance management system. This statewide performance management system is the cornerstone of the Department's organizational culture of accountability and performance excellence. The Department's Strategy and Performance Improvement Leadership (SPIL) Team consists of the Chief Operating Officer, state health office directors, and quality improvement liaisons, and is responsible for measuring, monitoring and reporting progress on the goals and objectives of the Agency Strategic Plan, State Health Improvement Plan, Quality Improvement Plan, and general performance management. The Team meets monthly to discuss recommendations about tools and methods that integrate performance management into sustainable business practices. Each objective has been assigned to a division within the agency (Appendix D) for implementation and quarterly reporting to Florida Health Performs. On a quarterly basis, the SPIL Team will review quarterly agency strategic plan tracking reports for progress toward goals. Annually, an agency strategic plan progress report will be developed by the team and presented to executive leadership, assessing progress toward reaching goals, objectives and achievements for the year. The Agency Strategic Plan will be reviewed by January each year, based on an assessment of availability of resources, data, community readiness, the current progress and the alignment of goals.

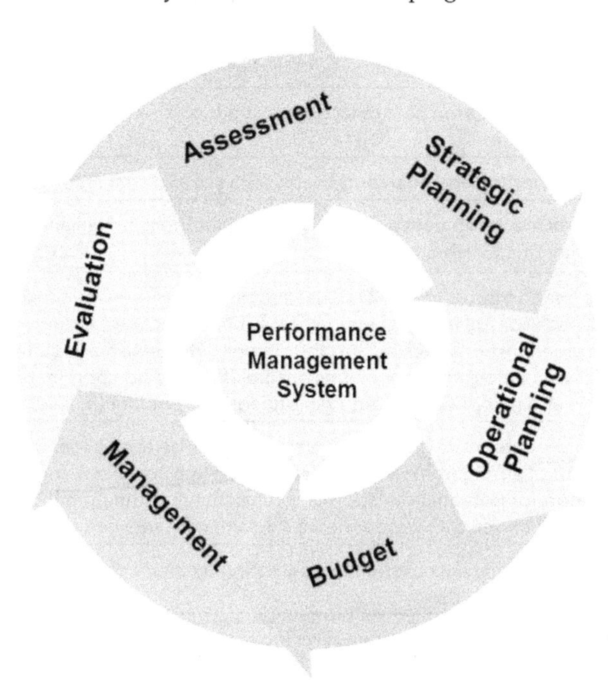

Leadership, Workforce and Infrastructure

APPENDIX C

Strengths, Weaknesses, Opportunities and Threats
Strengths
Investing in research, transparency in results, research symposiums
Our workforce is diverse and culturally competent
Partnerships at the state level and local level are strong and abundant
Every county has an active community health improvement planning partnership, and a community health improvement plan
Active and effective partnerships with stakeholders at the state level
Integrated agency that provides a statewide comprehensive public health system (i.e. lab, pharmacy, county health departments (CHDs), Children's Medical Services (CMS) clinics, health care practitioner regulation and licensing). The Department has its responsibilities outlined in Florida Statutes. There is a CHD in each of Florida's 67 counties. DOH is a centralized organization; the CHDs are part of the department.
The Division of Medical Quality Assurance has strong provider assessment capability
Physician and dental workforce assessments already completed
Florida's public health statutes have been recently reviewed and are keeping pace with scientific developments and current constitutional, legal and ethical changes
ESF8 response/strong preparedness infrastructure
Emerging technologies in health care including telemedicine and electronic health records create efficiencies and opportunities to expand services
The Department supports pilot and demonstration projects and has many model practices that can be shared
The Department purchases pharmaceuticals at federal pricing - resulting in cost savings
There are organizational processes in place that demonstrate commitment to performance management and improvement
Expertise in collecting, reporting and analyzing health statistics and vital records
Ability to collect and provide comparative data through Department surveillance systems and surveys (CHARTS, Merlin, BRFSS, HMS etc.)
We administer public health through 67 CHDs. They are the primary service providers in the areas of infectious disease control and prevention, family health services and environmental health services. Statewide functions such as the laboratories, Vital Statistics, a state pharmacy, disaster preparedness and emergency operations ensure efficient and coordinated approaches to monitoring diseases and responding to emerging needs at a population level
We have public health preparedness plans, partnerships, expertise and leadership in the health and medical component of all-hazards planning, preparation (including training and exercising), staff and material support for potential catastrophic events that may threaten the health of citizens and compromise our ability to deliver needed health care services
Committed to continuous quality improvement and creating a culture of quality, as evident by participation in accreditation activities
Effective marketing methods through programs like Tobacco Free Florida
Improved understanding of privacy and confidentiality laws and promoted coordination across programs and system wide

Weaknesses
Resources for training, continuing education, recruitment and retention
Succession planning, career ladders, advancement and leadership opportunities
Lack of resources prioritized for program monitoring/evaluation and quality improvement activities
Barriers to internal communication; reluctance to express opinions that may be contrary to current policy
Number of health care providers in rural areas
Decreasing CHD capacity to provide locally needed services
Lack of comprehensive evaluation of health communications, health education and promotion interventions
Lack of standards for health communication and resource materials to reach targeted populations with culturally and linguistically appropriate messaging
Increased demand for services without the capacity to meet the demand; resources are shrinking as a result of the economy
Lack of standard process maps for administrative and financial processes
Inconsistent conduction of periodic reviews on the effectiveness of the state surveillance systems
Opportunities
National awareness for healthier lifestyles and interest in workplace wellness programs
Recruitment of health care practitioners and public health professionals
Re-assess, re-evaluate health care practitioner assessments that DOH performs
Leverage partnerships among agencies and institutions of higher learning to enhance and improve current workforce capacity in order to support education of future public health professionals
Educate public and policy makers about public health
Participation in proposing changes to regulations
Use effective, evidence-based strategies and model practices
Include health impact assessments in planning
Telemedicine use to expand services
Robust public health statutes
Partnerships with non-profit hospitals to conduct community health needs assessments and preventative activities
Common priority health issues among state and locals present opportunities for system wide support and collaboration
Implement reviews of partnership development activities and their effectiveness
Regionalize the processing of accounts payable, billing, human resources and purchasing
Increased opportunity for the population to be insured
Shift in clinical practices locally to population health prevention services
Shift in public awareness and interest in social determinants of health
Leverage Medicaid managed care for public health improvement
Collaborating with tribal health councils

Ability to increase preventative dental services
Broader knowledge and promotion of health in all policies, especially in urban planning (e.g. smart growth, multi-modal transportation, etc.)
Increase leveraging of the Medicaid Family Planning Waiver program. This Waiver program allows women who have had a recent Medicaid paid service to retain coverage for family planning services for up to two years. Since over half of births in Florida were covered by Medicaid, this covers many women. The prevention of an unplanned pregnancy or another pregnancy in close proximity to a recent birth has the potential to lower infant mortality and reduce public assistance costs. CHDs do the eligibility determination for the Family Planning Waiver and can influence participation in this program through outreach.
Partner with DOE and the local school systems to increase physical activity among children and nutrition in the schools. Encourage after-school programs to emphasize physical activity, issue awards for physical activity efforts, grade schools on their commitment to encouraging healthy behaviors on the part of their students, etc.
Threats
Aging population
Funding cuts to programs and FTEs
Fewer benefits for workers
Shortage of health care providers
Emerging geographic health care shortage areas
Increased demands for care due to demographic shifts and economic situations
Program and funding cuts shift burdens to other segments of the public health system
Increased need for behavioral health services
Overuse of emergency rooms for primary care
Changes in educational practice and school curriculum impacts learning healthy lifestyles
Improved technology has encouraged more sedentary lifestyles, particularly among children
Emerging public health threats including infectious diseases, natural disasters and concurrent complacency in terms of family and business preparedness planning
Lack of residency slots for practitioners educated in Florida
No reciprocity for dental licenses in Florida
Inconsistent behavioral health services across counties
Need to improve health status and reduce disparities in chronic diseases, tobacco use, overweight/obesity, low physical activity levels, diabetes, unintentional injury, prescription drug abuse, infant mortality and prematurity, unintended and teen pregnancy, breastfeeding, child abuse/neglect, adverse childhood events, oral health, depression and behavioral health, adult substance abuse, HIV, influenza, access to care, and emerging health issues.
The transition to population health from clinical reduces the Department's ability to respond to infectious disease outbreaks, such as H1N1, without relying on partnership and volunteer professionals
The Department is challenged to compete against the marketing capabilities of the fast food industry, the soft drink industry, etc. The efforts of these entities offset our Healthy Behavior marketing activities.
Florida continues to host a substantial number of medically uninsured persons who have lesser access to health care due in part to a large service and construction industry. Although the economy is recovering many of the new jobs pay low wages and do not provide health insurance.
Good health is often a lesser priority among some Floridians

APPENDIX D

Work Plan and Alignment

Objective	Economic Develop.	2016 LRPP	SHIP	Assigned to	Source
By 12/31/2018, reduce the three-year rolling average of black infant mortality rate from 10.9 (2012-2014) to 8.3 per 1,000 live births and reduce black-white infant mortality gap from 2.25 to less than 2 times higher or reduce the black-white infant mortality gap by 12%.		1B	AC5.4.4	DCHP	CHARTS & Annual state vital statist cs report, June
By 12/31/2018, increase the percentage of children in grade 1 who are at a healthy weight from 66% (2013) to 70%.			CD1.2.2	DCHP	FY 2013-14, Growth and Development Screening with Body Mass Index
By 12/31/2018, increase the percentage of adults in Florida who are at a healthy weight from 35% (2013) to 38%.		2A	CD1.2.1	DCHP	Annual BRFSS
By 12/31/2018, reduce the number of adults who report ever being told they had coronary heart disease, heart attack, or stroke from 10.3% (2013) to 9.8%.			CD3.2.0	DCHP	Annual BRFSS
By 12/31/2018, reduce the rate of new cancer from 424.6 (2012) to 400 per 100,000.			CD3.2.0	DCHP	Florida Cancer Data System
By 12/31/2018, decrease the unintentional injury crude death rate from 46.7 (2014) to 38.7 per 100,000.		2G	Goal HP4	DEPCS	DeathStat Database
By 12/31/2018, reduce the annual number of newly diagnosed HIV infections in Florida from 4,613 (2014) to 4,255.		2B	HP1.3.4	DDCHP	eHARS
By 12/31/2018, reduce the annual number of newly diagnosed HIV infections in Florida's black population from 2,024 (2014) to 1,867.		2B	HP1.3.7	DDCHP	eHARS
By 12/31/2018, increase the proportion of ADAP clients with an undetectable viral load from 89% (2014) to 92%.	Goal 3	2B	HP1.3.5	DDCHP	eHARS & ADAP Database

Objective	Economic Develop.	2016 LRPP	SHIP	Assigned to	Source
By 12/31/2018, reduce the rate per 100,000 of total early syphilis in Florida from 18.5 (2014) to 17.9.			HP1.2.0	DDCHP	PRISM
By 12/31/2018, establish five partnerships for developing activities that can impact the incidence of Alzheimer's disease and related dementias.				DCHP	Community Engagement Ad hoc Reports
By 12/31/2018, increase the percent of 2 year olds who are fully immunized from 86% (2014) to 90%.	Goal 3	3C	HP1.1.1	DDCHP	FL SHOTS
By 12/31/2018, increase percent of teens who have completed the first HPV shot from 57.2% (2014) to 70%.			HP1.1.0	DDCHP	National Immunization Survey
By 12/31/2018, convert all 88 facilities using flat files to HL7 from ESSENCE.			HP1.4.5 HI1.3.3	DDCHP	ESSENCE Report
By 12/31/2018, increase the number of hospitals participating in electronic lab reporting (ELR) from 52 (2014) to 110.			HP1.4.4 HI1.3.1	DDCHP	ELR-OLAP
By 12/31/2018, increase Florida's National Health Security Preparedness Index (NHSPI) score from 7.8 (2014) to 8.1.		3A	HP3.3.0	DEPCS	NHSPI Index
By 12/31/2018, decrease current inhaled nicotine prevalence in Florida youth age 11-17 from 14.7% (2014) to 12.6%.		3B	CD4.2.4	DCHP	Middle School Health Behavior Survey & Florida Youth Tobacco Survey
By 12/31/2018, decrease current inhaled nicotine prevalence in adults from 21.3% (2014) to 19.2%.			CD4.2.2	DCHP	Florida Adult Tobacco Survey
By 06/30/2018, increase communication products from 3000 (2015) to 3600.				OC	Meltwater Report
By 12/31/2018, increase participation of DOH employees in one or more professional development opportunities to 50%.			HI3.1.0	DA	PeopleFirst Performance Report
By June 30, 2016, 100% of programs will operate within their annual operating budgets				OBRM	OBRM Quarterly Report

Objective	Economic Develop.	2016 LRPP	SHIP	Assigned to	Source
By 12/31/2016, complete a comparative analysis of agency IT expenditure.			HI1.0.0	OIT	IT Report
By 12/31/2016, implement the operational plan for Human Resources Consortiums.				DA	HR Action Plans
By 12/31/2016, provide evidence for value/ROI for consolidating billing functions.			HI2.1.4	DA	HR Action Plans
By 12/31/2017, reduce administrative costs associated with Title XIX and Title XXI to 6.5-8.0% of plan expenditures.	Strategy 25	2C	AC6.0.0	DCMS	CMS Plan Admin Cost Analysis
By 12/31/2018, publish 5 articles regarding the Department's accomplishments in peer-reviewed journals.				DCHP	Publication report
By 06/30/2016, reduce the number of lines of regulation by 15% from 71,442 (2015) to 60,725.				OGC	Rules Query
By 12/31/2017, reduce by 50% the percentage of deficient applications received from 74% (2015) to 37%.	Goal 1		AC2.1.3	DMQA	MQA Quarterly Reports
By 12/31/2016, increase the number of applications approved for health care licensure of military spouses and honorably discharged veterans by 50% from 137 (2015) to 206.	Goal 1		AC2.1.0	DMQA	MQA Quarterly Reports
By 12/31/2017, establish enterprise solutions for all department regulatory functions.		5B		DMQA	MQA Action Plan
By 12/31/2016, ensure that 3 of 4 quarterly (FL disability) claim processing times are less than the national average processing time.		4A		DDD	Federal DDD Quarterly Report

DA Division of Administration
DCHP Division of Community Health Promotion
DCMS Division of Children's Medical Services
DDCHP Division of Disease Control and Health Protection
DDD Division of Disability Determinations
DEPCS Division of Emergency Preparedness and Community Support
LRPP Long Range Program Plan
DMQA Division of Medical Quality Assurance
OBRM Office of Budget and Revenue Management
OC Office of Communications
OGC Office of the General Counsel
OIT Office of Information Technology
SHIP State Health Improvement Plan
Economic Develop. Florida Strategic Plan for Economic Development

APPENDIX E

Environmental Scan Resources

1. 2015 State Themes and Strengths Assessment
2. Assessment of 67 current county strategic plans
3. Agency strategic plan status report
4. Alzheimer's disease Facts and Figures 2015
5. Alzheimer's Disease Research Grant Advisory Board Annual Report FY 2014 -2015
6. Assessment of County Health Department Immunization Coverage Levels in Two-Year-Old Children 2015
7. Behavioral Risk Factor Surveillance System (BRFSS) 2013
8. Biomedical Research Advisory Council Annual Report 2013-2014
9. Florida Community Health Assessment Resource Tool Set (CHARTS)
10. Division of Medical Quality Assurance Annual Report and Long Range Plan FY 2013-2014
11. Employee Satisfaction Survey 2015 results
12. Florida Department of Health, Long Range Program Plan 2015-16 through 2019-20
13. Florida Department of Health, Office of Inspector General Annual Report FY 2013-2014
14. Florida Department of Health, Year in Review 2013-2014
15. Florida Middle School Health Behavior Survey Results for 2013
16. Florida Morbidity Statistics Report, 2013
17. Florida Pregnancy Risk Assessment Monitoring System Trend Report 2000-2011 Executive Summary
18. Florida Strategic Plan for Economic Development
19. Florida Vital Statistics Annual Report 2014
20. Florida Youth Risk Behavior Survey Results for 2013
21. Florida Youth Tobacco Survey Results for 2014
22. Health Status Assessment 2015
23. Healthiest weight state profile
24. Leading causes of injury
25. Leading rankable causes of death
26. Physician Workforce Annual Report 2014
27. State monthly economic updates
28. Tuberculosis Control Section Report 2013
29. Volunteer Health Services Annual Report 2012-2013

REFERENCES

Florida Department of Health. (2017). Florida Department of Health agency strategic plan 2016-2018. Retrieved from http://www.floridahealth.gov/about-the-department-of-health/_documents/agency-strategic-plan.pdf

Health Resources and Services Administration. (n.d.) Strategic plan FY 2016-FY 2018. Retrieved from https://www.hrsa.gov/about/strategic-plan/index.html

INDEX

CPSIA information can be obtained
at www.ICGtesting.com
Printed in the USA
BVHW010530220322
632015BV00016B/286